W9-BCF-022

BRAZING MANUAL

Prepared by

Committee on Brazing and Soldering
AMERICAN WELDING SOCIETY

REINHOLD PUBLISHING CORPORATION
NEW YORK
CHAPMAN & HALL, LTD., LONDON

COPYRIGHT 1955 BY
AMERICAN WELDING SOCIETY
33 WEST 39TH STREET
NEW YORK 18, N. Y.

All rights reserved

Third Printing 1960

Library of Congress Catalog Card Number: 55-9167

REINHOLD PUBLISHING CORPORATION

Publishers of Chemical Engineering Catalog, Chemical Materials Catalog, "Automatic Control," "Materials & Methods"; Advertising Management American Chemical Society

PRINTED IN THE USA BY WAVERLY PRESS

TT
267
A53

PERSONNEL OF AWS COMMITTEE ON BRAZING AND SOLDERING

A. N. Kugler, *Chairman*....................Air Reduction Sales Co.

R. M. Wilson, Jr., *Vice Chairman*...........The International Nickel Co., Inc.

S. A. Greenberg, *Secretary*.................American Welding Society

L. E. Abbott.............................Bell Telephone Laboratories, Inc.

J. H. Adams, Jr..........................Stanley G. Flagg and Company, Inc.

R. E. Ballentine.........................Westinghouse Electric Corp.

J. O. Barlon............................Collins Radio Co.

O. T. Barnett...........................Armour Research Foundation of Illinois Institute of Technology

D. M. Borcina...........................Lead Industries Association

Bureau of Ships.........................Navy Department

J. G. Christ............................Westinghouse Electric Corp.

R. M. Evans............................Battelle Memorial Institute

B. A. Hackett (J. G. Landrigan, *Alternate*)...United Wire and Supply Co.

L. H. Hawthorne.........................Revere Copper and Brass Incorporated

C. L. Hibert............................Consolidated Vultee Aircraft

G. O. Hoglund...........................Aluminum Co. of America

F. W. Hussey............................Frankford Arsenal

(J. K. McDowell, *Alternate*)............Rock Island Arsenal

J. Imperati............................American Brass Co.

H. V. Inskeep..........................Linde Air Products Co.

C. E. Johnson..........................Scaife Co.

P. Klain..............................The Dow Chemical Co.

R. M. MacIntosh (R. J. Nekervis, *Alternate*)..Tin Research Institute, Inc

R. O. McIntosh.........................Westinghouse Electric Corp.

iii

R. L. Peaslee...........................Wall Colmonoy Corp.

M. A. Pugacz...........................General Electric Co.

A. M. Setapen (C. H. Chatfield, *Alternate*)...Handy and Harman

W. J. Van Natten......................General Electric Co.

J. J. Vreeland.........................Chase Brass and Copper Co.

W. J. Wagnitz (A. S. Cross, *Alternate*).......American Platinum Works

R. D. Wasserman (W. Kriewall, *Alternate*)....Eutectic Welding Alloys Corp.

K. M. Weigert..........................Goldsmith Bros. Smelting and Refining Co.

J. R. Wirt.............................General Motors Corp.

INTRODUCTION

A common understanding of the basic terminology in any field is a prerequisite for clarity of thought and expression and for constructive discussion concerning its technology. There has always existed some confusion in the use of the words welding, brazing, and soldering. To clarify this situation the A.W.S. has adopted the word *welding* as a generic term to cover the joining of metals by the application of heat. This by definition makes arc welding and brazing, subdivisions of welding in its general sense. It must be kept in mind that once an adjective or prefix is attached to the word welding such as arc, gas, atomic hydrogen, etc., the word welding loses its generic meaning and connotes one of the processes or group of processes of welding or of achieving a metal joint by the application of heat.

Welding processes may be classified in a number of ways. The need is best met by taking existing terminology and fitting it into a general outline under welding to make what is known more easily and quickly grasped and also form a sounder basis for further progress, both empirically in the shop and scientifically in the laboratory; and further, to make it easier for these two groups to exchange information. The AWS Master Chart of Welding Processes shows all of the welding processes which are of industrial significance. The "Welding Handbook," Third Edition, includes the standard welding terms and their definitions and by means of explanation throughout the book, does an admirable job of clarifying welding terminology.

This Manual confines its discussion to the brazing processes alone. The A.W.S. defines brazing as "A group of welding processes wherein coalescence is produced by heating to a suitable temperature above 800 F and by using a nonferrous filler metal, having a melting point below that of the base metals. The filler metal is distributed between the closely-fitted surfaces of the joint by capillary attraction."

The brazing definition is composed of three parts: (1) The coalescence, joining, or uniting of an assembly of two or more parts into one structure is achieved by heating the assembly or the region of the parts to be joined at a temperature of 800 F or above, plus (2) the use of a nonferrous filler metal with a melting range below that of the base metals, plus the qualification that (3) the filler metal must wet the base metals surfaces. The flow of filler metal in the joints by capillary attraction is predicated on this assumption.

This last factor most distinguishes the brazing processes from other welding processes.

To achieve a good joint by brazing using any of the various brazing processes described in this Manual, the following requirements must be considered and properly dealt with:

(1) *Precleaning.* The parts must be clean to enable proper brazing.

(2) *Fluxing.* A flux or cleansing atmosphere must be provided to either prevent oxidation by protection of the surface or dissolve or reduce any oxides formed.

(3) *Proper alignment.* The relative positions of the metals being joined must be properly maintained during heating and cooling of the assembly. This may or may not require fixtures depending upon the design of the part, the relative clearances involved and the brazing process.

(4) *Heating.* The brazing process must be selected which will provide the proper brazing temperature, heat distribution and rate of heating and cooling in keeping with the properties of the base metal and the requirements of the finished product.

(5) *Postcleaning.* If an atmosphere or unobjectionable flux is used no further cleaning may be necessary. If, however, a corrosive flux is used, it is important that it be thoroughly removed.

No analysis of a subject that is continuously being improved can hope to be complete. Nor can the subject be covered with the thoroughness which would satisfy the specialist. As is so often true of industrial operations, the art is ahead of the science. Thus the newcomer must, after studying what is available on the subject, apply the information to his particular application by trial and error. However, it is the hope of the Committee that his trials and errors will be fewer for having this Manual as a guide.

This Manual is limited to industrial applications involving brazing metal-to-metal assemblies. It does not cover brazing applications in the jewelry field, nor does it cover the joining of assemblies having nonmetallic components.

Comments, inquiries and suggestions for future revisions of this Manual are welcomed. Address them to Secretary, AWS Committee on Brazing and Soldering, American Welding Society, 33 West 39th Street, New York 18, New York.

CONTENTS

vii

Chapter 1

BRAZING PROCESSES, EQUIPMENT AND PROCEDURES

BRAZING PROCESSES AND EQUIPMENT

The master chart of welding processes (Fig. 1.1) lists eight subsidiary processes under Brazing as follows:

    (1) Torch Brazing
    (2) Twin-Carbon Arc Brazing
    (3) Furnace Brazing
    (4) Induction Brazing
    (5) Resistance Brazing
    (6) Dip Brazing
    (7) Block Brazing
    (8) Flow Brazing

Whatever the process used, the filler metal is nonferrous and has a melting point above 800 F, but below that of the base metal, and is distributed in the joint by capillary attraction.

Chapter 3 discusses the commonly used brazing filler metals and processes for different base metals.

Torch Brazing

As the name implies, torch brazing is accomplished by heating with a gas torch or torches. Depending upon the temperature and the amount of heat required, the fuel gas (acetylene, propane, city gas, etc.) may be burned with air, compressed air or oxygen.

Brazing filler metal may be preplaced in the forms of rings, washers, strips, slugs, powder, etc., or may be *face-fed*, that is, fed from hand-held filler metal, usually in the form of wire or rod. In any case proper cleaning and fluxing are essential.

For manual torch brazing the torch may be equipped with a single tip, Fig. 1.2, (single or multiflame). Manual torch brazing is particularly useful on assemblies involving sections of unequal mass. Machine operations can be set up where the rate of production warrants using one or more torches equipped with single or multiflame tips (Fig. 1.3). The machine may be

1

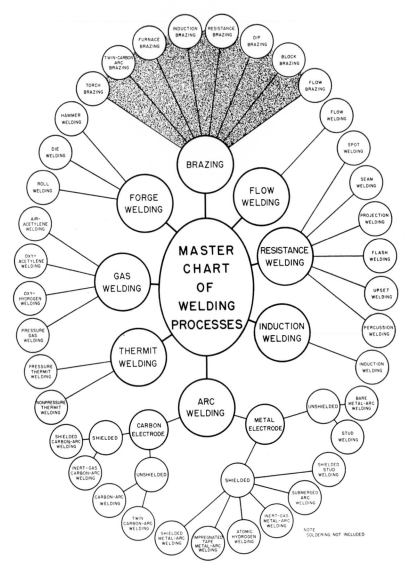

Figure 1.1. Master chart of welding processes

designed to move either the work or the torches or both. For premixed city gas-air flames the refractory-type burner is used (Fig. 1.4).

Twin-Carbon Arc Brazing

This process is not used extensively but provides a method of extremely rapid heating. The equipment consists of a holder so constructed that two

Figure 1.2. Manual torch brazing with a multiflame single tip

Figure 1.3. Machine brazing with multiple tips

Figure 1.4. Refractory type burner using city gas-air mixture

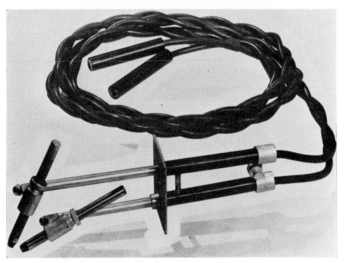

Figure 1.5. Manual twin-carbon arc brazing holder

graphite or carbon electrodes can be held at an angle and spaced to give a flaming arc (Fig. 1.5). The intense heat of this arc requires careful manipulation of the flame to prevent overheating when brazing. Because of this, machine twin-carbon arc brazing normally is not used. The electrical energy necessary to maintain the arc is obtained from either an ac or dc arc-welding machine. The brazing filler metal is usually face-fed.

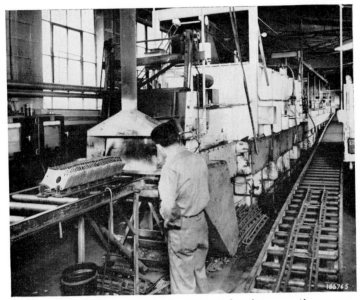

Figure 1.6. Conveyor-type furnace brazing operation

Furnace Brazing

Furnace brazing is used extensively where the parts to be brazed can be assembled with the filler metal preplaced near or in the joint. This process is particularly applicable for high production brazing. The preplaced brazing filler metal may be in the form of wire, foil, filings, slugs, powder, paste, etc. Fluxing is usually employed except when an atmosphere is specifically introduced in the furnace to perform the same function.

Furnaces for this process usually contain heating and cooling chambers and should have automatic time and temperature controls (Fig. 1.6). The heat may be obtained by electrical means or by gas or oil. The work may be placed in the furnace singly, in batches or on a continuous conveyer. Four types of furnaces are used: box type, conveyor type, retort type and bell type.

Induction Brazing

The heat necessary for brazing with this process is obtained from an electric current induced in the parts to be brazed, hence the name induction brazing. When induction brazing, the parts are placed in or near an alternating-current-carrying coil and do not form a part of the electrical circuit (Fig. 1.7).

The brazing filler metal is usually preplaced. Careful design of the joint

Figure 1.7. Induction brazing set-up

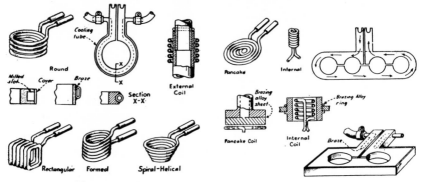

Figure 1.8. Typical induction brazing coils and plates

and the coil set-up are necessary to assure that the surfaces of all members of the joint reach the brazing temperature at the same time. Typical coil designs are shown in Fig. 1.8. Flux is usually employed except when an atmosphere is specifically introduced to perform the same function.

The three common sources of high-frequency electric current used for induction brazing are the motor-generator, resonant spark gap and vacuum tube oscillator.

Resistance Brazing

The heat necessary for resistance brazing is obtained from the resistance to the flow of an electric current through the electrodes and the joint to be brazed. The parts comprising the joint form a part of the electric circuit.

The brazing filler metal, in some convenient form, is preplaced or face-fed. Fluxing is done with due attention being paid to the conductivity of the fluxes. (Most fluxes are insulators when dry.) Flux is usually employed except when an atmosphere is specifically introduced to perform the same function.

The parts to be brazed are held between two electrodes and proper pressure and current applied. The pressure should be maintained until the joint has solidified. In some cases both electrodes may be located on the same side of the joint with a suitable backing to maintain the required pressure.

The equipment consists of tongs or clamps with the electrodes attached at the end of each arm (See Fig. 1.9). The arms are current-carrying conductors attached by leads to a transformer. Direct current may be used but is comparatively expensive. The tongs should preferably be water cooled to avoid overheating. Resistance welding machines are also used.

Figure 1.9. Resistance brazing with tongs

The electrodes may be carbon, graphite, refractory metals or copper alloys according to the required conductivity.

Dip Brazing

There are two methods of dip brazing: chemical bath dip brazing and molten metal bath dip brazing.

In chemical bath dip brazing the brazing filler metal, in suitable form, is preplaced and the assembly is immersed in a bath of molten salt. The salt bath furnishes the heat necessary for brazing and usually provides the necessary protection from oxidation; if not, a suitable flux should be used.

The salt bath is contained in a metal or other suitable pot, also called the furnace (Fig. 1.10), which is heated (1) from the outside through the wall of the pot, (2) by means of electrical resistance units placed in the bath, or (3) by the I^2R loss in the bath itself.

In molten metal bath dip brazing the parts are immersed in a bath of molten brazing filler metal contained in a suitable pot (Fig. 1.11). The

Figure 1.10. Chemical bath dip brazing

Figure 1.11. Molten metal bath dip brazing

parts must be cleaned and fluxed if necessary. A cover of flux should be maintained over the molten bath.

This method is largely confined to brazing small parts such as wires or narrow strips of metal. The ends of the wires or parts must be held firmly together when they are removed from the bath until the brazing filler metal has fully solidified.

Block Brazing

In block brazing the heat for brazing is derived from large metal blocks (hence the name) which are separately heated and applied to the work. The heated blocks impart sufficient heat to raise the parts to brazing temperature and cause the brazing filler metal to flow. The brazing filler metal is usually preplaced.

Flow Brazing

Flow brazing is a process in which molten brazing filler metal is poured onto the joint, preferably from one side. This process is giving way to other brazing processes which are more economical and efficient.

Special Processes

In several industrial applications, like the manufacture of electron tubes, the usual brazing processes described above are used with certain particular refinements. (See Chapter 9.) The use of a vacuum furnace is an illustration of this. The refinements used are determined in each case according to the special requirements of that application and so cannot be adequately covered by basic information given in this book. The special features of such cases have been pointed out elsewhere in this book.

BRAZING PROCEDURES

The function of a recorded brazing procedure is to establish all the conditions and limits of the variables of the procedure to the end that the brazed products will be uniform and in compliance with the design requirements. A recorded brazing procedure is valuable in that it provides a positive means of conveying the intentions of the designer to the production department with assurance that the instructions will be clearly understood. A recorded brazing procedure can also be used for inspection purposes in determining whether the instructions are being followed in production. For example, an inspector can, by referring to the recorded brazing procedure, determine what base and filler metals are to be used and can verify that they are being used in production. A recorded brazing procedure can be filed upon completion of a job and referred to again later when a similar production job occurs. A suggested form for recording brazing procedures is shown in Fig. 1.12. All of the factors listed there may not apply for every job, in which case they are merely omitted. Those items which do apply should be covered in such detail as is necessary to accomplish the desired results.

The following is a discussion of each item shown in Fig. 1.12. It is intended as a guide to proper and complete recording of brazing procedures:

Sketch. The sketch should show all geometric details of the joint, including tolerances, where required. It may be of only the joint area or of the complete assembly.

Base Metal. Use ASTM, AISI, SAE, MIL or other standard specification numbers. If standard specifications are not applicable give chemical analysis, trade name or other positive identification. For dissimilar combinations each base metal should be identified. Special conditions of the base metal (temper, finish, etc.) should also be specified.

Precleaning. Specify complete precleaning procedure. State time between cleaning and brazing, if important, and any special handling requirements to avoid contamination. Plating to be specified only if used to facilitate brazing.

Filler Metal. Preferably use classification numbers in Specifications for Brazing Filler Metal (AWS Number A5.8; ASTM Number B260). Also give size and form. Also specify how applied, i.e., face fed, preplaced, etc. Refer to sketch if necessary.

Flux or Atmosphere. In addition to positive identification as to type

Brazing Procedure No._____

Joint_____

(Insert sketch here showing shape and
thickness of parts, joint clearance,
placement of filler metal and assembly
of joint including jigging or fixtures.)

Base Metal(s): _____

(Specify Specification number or other identification.)

Precleaning: _____

_____

(Specify cleaner to be used: wire brush, emery or name or composition of cleaner. Also specify cleaning procedure including time, temperature, rinsing, etc. Specify plating operations, if used.)

Filler Metal: _____

(Specify Classification Number or other identification and size and form.)

Flux or Atmosphere: _____
(Specify AWS Type No. or other identification and location and means of application.)

Brazing Process: _____

_____

_____

(Specify process and other details such as brazing temperature; preheat temperature, if required; tip size and fuel gas for torch brazing; current and pressure for resistance brazing; frequency and coil type and number for induction brazing; etc.)

Postbraze Cleaning: _____
(Specify cleaner to be used and rinse.)

Postbraze Heat Treatment: _____
(Other than coincident with brazing; specify rate of heating, temperature, cooling rate, etc.)

Inspection Requirements: _____

_____

_____

(Specify test requirements, frequency of sampling for inspection, tests to be used and details of tests such as pressure for pressure test, extent of permissible defects for radiography, size of fillet, etc.)

Remarks:*
(Insert here special precautions, techniques and other pertinent information not otherwise covered.)

* This item appears on the reverse side of the form.

Figure 1.12. Proposed form for recording brazing procedures

11

Figure 1.13. Use of form for recording brazing procedures
(For illustration only)

Brazing Procedure No._____A_____
Joint____102_____

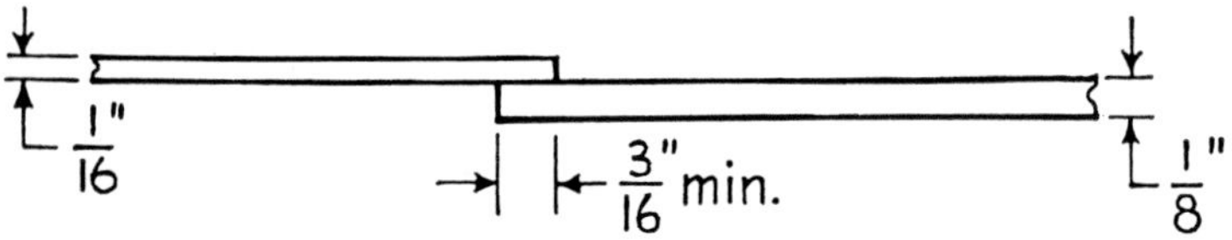

Base Metal(s): ___Top—Deoxidized copper; Bottom—1020 Steel_____
                (Specify Specification number or other identification.)

Precleaning: ___Immersion in Greasoff "A" for 19 min., dry; remove scale completely___
with 000 emery cloth.

(Specify cleaner to be used: wire brush, emery or name or composition of cleaner. Also
specify cleaning procedure including time, temperature, rinsing, etc. Specify plating
operations, if used.)

Filler Metal: ___BAg-1_____
               (Specify Classification Number or other identification and size and form.)

Flux or Atmosphere: ___AWS Type 3 Flux_____
(Specify AWS Type No. or other identification and location and means of application.)

Brazing Process: ___Torch braze using oxy-acetylene flame without preheat. Use #4 tip,___
4 psi oxygen and 4 psi acetylene pressure. (Specify make of torch.) Concentrate heat on copper
member. Complete penetration required.

(Specify process and other details such as brazing temperature; preheat temperature, if
required; tip size and fuel gas for torch brazing; current and pressure for resistance
brazing; frequency and coil type and number for induction brazing; etc.)

Postbraze Cleaning: ___Permit joint to cool to 900 F, then immerse in cold water. Brush___
                     (Specify cleaner to be used and rinse.)
                 joint to remove any flux residue. Complete flux removal essential.

Postbraze Heat Treatment: None
(Other than coincident with brazing; specify rate of heating, temperature, cooling
rate, etc.)

Inspection Requirements: Visual inspection of each joint to ascertain complete penetration
with fillet on each side. Destructive tension test of 1 in each 100 pieces. Joint must
fail in copper at not less than 28,000 psi.

(Specify test requirements, frequency of sampling for inspection, tests to be used and
details of tests such as pressure for pressure test, extent of permissible defects for
radiography, size of fillet, etc.)

Remarks:*
    (Insert here special precautions, techniques and other pertinent information
    not otherwise covered.)
                                    None

* This item appears on the reverse side of the form.

12

specify how applied and other special conditions such as dryness of atmosphere. If both flux and atmosphere are used, both should be specified.

Brazing Process. First the brazing process should be specified, i.e., torch, furnace, induction, dip, etc. All of the detailed information necessary to control the process should then be given. This would include type and size of tip for torch brazing, type of furnace for furnace brazing, etc. If heat is to be applied at a particular area or to be avoided at some other area, this should be carefully described.

Postbraze Cleaning. It is usually necessary to remove all traces of flux residue, particularly where corrosive fluxes are used such as for aluminum and magnesium. In other cases it may be a matter of appearance or of importance for purposes of finishing.

Postbraze Heat Treatment. If a heat treatment is performed concurrent with the brazing operation the necessary information should be included under the heading "Brazing Process." Other heat treatments should be specified here.

Inspection Requirements. Full details should be specified as to the test or tests to be used, the details of testing and the test results. The frequency of sampling for testing should also be specified. The extent to which defective joints may be repaired or are rejected should also be defined.

Fig. 1.13 shows an example of a complete form for recording a brazing procedure. *It is important to note that this procedure is used for illustration only and does not indicate good commercial practice.*

Chapter 2

PROPERTIES OF BASE METALS

Chemical Analysis, Mechanical Properties, Physical Constants

Appendix A lists the chemical analysis, mechanical properties and physical constants of many engineering materials which can be brazed. The information is necessarily condensed, and is included to give a source for quick reference. Where more exact information is required, reference to the supplier of the material, to competent engineering handbooks, or to applicable specifications should be made. The data in Appendix A should not be used for critical design or specification purposes.

The metals and alloys are grouped together according to their main constituents. The names employed are those most commonly used in industry. The chemical analysis shows the average value or the range of the main constituents. No attempt has been made to include the average value or permissible ranges of minor constituents.

The mechanical properties are average values obtained for some forms in which the materials are available and are expressed in units commonly used for these materials.

Metallurgical Considerations

All of the metals and alloys listed in Appendix A can be brazed when the proper procedure is employed. Some of the metals and alloys exhibit peculiar metallurgical phenomena which require special procedures to obtain satisfactory brazed assemblies.

Some of the metallurgical phenomena which will require special procedures are briefly described in the following paragraphs:

Hydrogen Embrittlement. Hydrogen is able to diffuse through many metals quite rapidly because of its small atomic size. The rate of diffusion increases as the temperature increases. When hydrogen diffuses into a metal which has not been completely deoxidized it may reduce the oxide of the metal if the temperature is high enough. Metallic sponge and water vapor are the end products of this reaction.

Because the molecular size of water vapor is too large to permit diffusion to the surface in the same manner as the hydrogen entered, a pressure is developed which has been calculated for tough pitch copper to be as high as 90,000 psi. These extremely high pressures literally tear the metal apart

14

by starting many small fissures or blisters, mainly at the grain boundaries. Metal which has been hydrogen embrittled exhibits lowered tensile properties.

Electrolytic tough pitch copper and silver and palladium, when they contain oxygen, are subject to hydrogen embrittlement if heated in the presence of hydrogen. If tough pitch copper is to be brazed without embrittlement, hydrogen must not be present in the heating atmosphere. It is better practice to use deoxidized copper or oxygen-free copper where brazing is to be done. Oxygen-free copper may be oxidized and become subject to hydrogen embrittlement if improperly heated. It is not practical to salvage hydrogen embrittled copper.

Steel is also subject to a form of hydrogen embrittlement, but of a different type. Hydrogen diffuses into steel in the same manner as in copper but it tends to accumulate in small voids such as those found around non-metallic inclusions and at grain boundaries. Water vapor is not formed, as in copper, but a high pressure is sometimes developed because the hydrogen diffuses in the atomic form, combines with other hydrogen atoms to the molecular form which is less mobile, and then remains trapped at such discontinuities. Steel which has been hydrogen embrittled shows low ductility when stressed. Fortunately, however, steel and other ferrous alloys may be salvaged by allowing the hydrogen to diffuse out by baking at only slightly elevated temperatures (180 to 212 F), or by permitting the steel to stand for long periods of time until the ductility is regained.

Fortunately, most other metals and alloys whose oxides may be reduced by hydrogen contain an excess amount of deoxidizing elements and are not subject to hydrogen embrittlement.

Carbide Precipitation. Some stainless steels and other alloys which contain chromium and carbon, are subject to carbide precipitation if heated to temperatures between 900 and 1300 F. Carbide precipitation means that the carbon combines preferentially with the chromium and is rejected as chromium carbide, usually at the grain boundaries. The alloy material immediately adjacent to the carbide particle, being depleted in chromium content, is no longer as corrosion resistant as the original metal. In certain corrosive environments the mechanical properties may be impaired with little or no apparent surface attack.

Precipitated carbides may be redissolved by heat treating at 1850 to 2050 F followed by rapid cooling. However, this treatment is not usually applicable to brazed assemblies.

Another stabilizing treatment which disperses the unprecipitated chromium uniformly throughout the structure is to heat to 1600 F for 2 hours followed by furnace cooling to 1000 F and subsequent air cooling.

If the brazing can be done very rapidly no appreciable amount of carbides will be precipitated with the normal types of stainless steels. Where this cannot be done and it is necessary to braze stainless steels for corrosive service, one of the stabilized compositions, such as Type 347 or 321, or the extra-low-carbon grades (ELC) should be used.

Stress Cracking. Many high strength materials like stainless steels, nickel alloys and copper-nickel alloys have a tendency to crack during brazing when in a highly stressed condition and in contact with molten brazing filler metal. Materials which have high annealing temperatures, and particularly those which are age-hardenable, are subject to this stress cracking phenomenon. The cracking occurs almost instantaneously during the brazing operation and is usually readily visible since the molten brazing filler metal follows the crack and completely fills it.

The process may be described as stress-corrosion cracking where the molten filler metal is considered as the corrosive medium. Stressed steel in a caustic solution or stressed brass in an ammonia solution are common examples. Sufficient stress to cause stress cracking can be produced by cold work prior to brazing, or by an externally applied stress from mechanical or thermal sources during the brazing operation.

When stress cracking is encountered its cause can usually be determined from a critical analysis of the brazing procedure. The usual remedy is to remove the source of stress. Stress cracking has been eliminated by:

(a) Using annealed temper rather than hard temper material.

(b) Annealing cold worked parts prior to brazing.

(c) Removing the source of externally applied stress, such as parts that do not fit properly, jigs that exert stress on the parts, or overhanging unsupported weights. (See Chapter 8.)

(d) Redesigning parts or revising joint design. (See Chapter 6.)

(e) Heating at a slower rate. Heavy parts can be heated so rapidly that stresses are set up by steep thermal gradients.

(f) Heating the fluxed and assembled parts, in a torch brazing application, to a high enough temperature to effect stress relief; cooling to the brazing temperature and then hand feeding the filler metal.

(g) Selecting a brazing filler metal which is less likely to induce this type of damage. (See Chapter 3.)

Fig. 2.1 shows stress cracking in deep drawn "K" Monel produced by brazing copper studs to a "K" Monel flange using BAg filler metal. Note that the cracks emerge from the brazing area into the base metal. The cracks are readily visible since they are outlined in the color of the silver filler metal.

Sulfur Embrittlement. Nickel and certain alloys containing appreciable amounts of nickel, if heated in the presence of sulfur, or compounds containing sulfur, may become embrittled. A low-melting nickel sulphide

Figure 2.1. Stress cracking in "K" Monel

is formed preferentially at the grain boundaries and, being brittle, will crack if subsequently stressed. Material so embrittled must be scrapped. It cannot be salvaged.

Nickel and nickel-copper alloys are most subject to this attack while those containing chromium are less subject to attack. It is important, however, that alloys in which nickel is the major component, be clean and free of sulfur-containing materials such as oil, grease, paint, crayon marks and drawing lubricants prior to heating and that heating be done only in a relatively sulfur-free atmosphere.

Phosphorus Embrittlement. Phosphorus combines with many metals to form brittle compounds known as phosphides. Brazing filler metal containing phosphorus must not be used with any iron or nickel-base alloy or alloys containing more than 5 per cent of either component.

Vapor Pressure. Special attention must be given to the selection of brazing filler metals when the brazed joint is to function in a vacuum. This condition prevails in several industries but applies particularly to electron tubes of larger size, such as power tubes, and to continuously-pumped structures of which particle acclerators, vacuum furnaces and coating units are examples. In all these devices a high vacuum is either necessary for satisfactory operation or required prior to the introduction of a desired gas atmosphere. Any components in the system which give off undesirable gases or vapors at any temperature encountered during processing or operation will spoil the vacuum and make the device inoperative sooner or later.

Table 2.1 gives melting points and vapor pressures at several temperatures for some elements of common brazing filler metals and base metals.

TABLE 2.1. MELTING POINTS AND VAPOR PRESSURES OF SOME METALS

Metal	Chemical Symbol	Melting Point		Vapor Pressure in mm Hg at T°			
		°C	°F	20°C	500°C	1000°C	2000°C
Aluminum	Al	658	1216	$<10^{-8}$	$<10^{-8}$	5×10^{-4}	150
Cadmium	Cd	321	610	$\sim 10^{-8}$	20	2500	Very high
Columbium	Cb	2500	4532	$<10^{-8}$	$<10^{-8}$	$<10^{-8}$	$<10^{-5}$
Copper	Cu	1083	1981	$<10^{-8}$	10^{-7}	10^{-4}	15
Gold	Au	1062.4	1945	$<10^{-8}$	10^{-7}	10^{-5}	40
Iron	Fe	1535	2795	$<10^{-8}$	$<10^{-8}$	10^{-6}	10
Lead	Pb	327	621	$<10^{-8}$	10^{-5}	2	1000
Magnesium	Mg	651	1204	$<10^{-8}$	8×10^{-2}	400	Very high
Molybdenum	Mo	2620	4748	$<10^{-8}$	$<10^{-8}$	$<10^{-8}$	10^{-4}
Nickel	Ni	1455	2651	$<10^{-8}$	$<10^{-8}$	10^{-7}	3
Phosphorus	P	44	232	$\sim 10^{-7}$	10,000	Very high	Very high
Platinum	Pt	1773.5	3223	$<10^{-8}$	$<10^{-8}$	$<10^{-8}$	$<10^{-2}$
Rhodium	Rh	1966	3571	$<10^{-8}$	$<10^{-8}$	$<10^{-8}$	$<10^{-3}$
Silver	Ag	960.5	1761	$<10^{-8}$	10^{-7}	10^{-1}	1000
Tantalum	Ta	2996	5425	$<10^{-8}$	$<10^{-8}$	$<10^{-8}$	$<10^{-8}$
Tin	Sn	232	450	$<10^{-8}$	$<10^{-8}$	4×10^{-4}	80
Tungsten	W	3370	6098	$<10^{-8}$	$<10^{-8}$	$<10^{-8}$	$<10^{-8}$
Zinc	Zn	419	786	$<10^{-8}$	1	2000	Very high

For vacuum tube applications zinc and cadmium cannot be permitted as components.

Oxide Stability. The oxides of most metals and alloys are quite easily fluxed in the presence of the proper flux or reduced in a reducing atmosphere. Oxides of chromium, aluminum, titanium, silicon, magnesium, manganese and beryllium are more difficult to remove and alloys containing these elements usually require some special treatment.

Chromium oxide is quite easily removed with a fluoride-bearing flux but cannot be reduced by hydrogen unless the atmosphere is very dry (about -70 F dew point) and only at high temperatures (in the range of 2000 F).

Aluminum, titanium, silicon, magnesium, manganese and beryllium oxides can also be removed by special fluxes but cannot be reduced in hydrogen atmospheres with usual brazing techniques. (See Chapter 4.) It is important, therefore, that special fluxes be employed when brazing materials which contain appreciable quantities of these elements.

Heat-Affected Zone. The heat employed for brazing affects the properties of the base metals being joined. Base metals whose mechanical properties were obtained by cold reduction (hard tempers) may soften or the grain size may increase if the brazing temperature is above their annealing temperatures. Base metals whose mechanical properties were obtained by thermal treatment may be altered by the brazing operation. Material in the annealed condition will generally experience no appreciable change due to brazing.

The zone through which these changes may occur will be dependent largely upon the process used. Torch, induction or dip brazing will produce some heat-affected zone. Furnace brazing affects all material in the furnace. In general, the heat-affected zone from brazing is wider and less sharply defined than that obtained by other welding processes.

Postbrazing Thermal Treatment. It is frequently desirable to give brazed assemblies a postbrazing thermal treatment to improve mechanical properties. In ferrous alloys this entails quenching from an elevated temperature followed by a draw at some lower temperature. In other alloys such as beryllium copper, "Duranickel," "K" Monel, Inconel "X" and Stainless 17-7PH it consists of heating for a period of time to some intermediate temperature followed by a controlled rate of cooling.

When a metal must be brazed and a subsequent thermal treatment performed. it is important that the brazing filler metal selected have sufficient strength at the thermal treatment temperatures to withstand the necessary handling.

Alloying and Diffusion. Brazing filler metals adhere to base metals by alloying and diffusion. Normally, such alloying is a surface effect and extends only a few thousandths of an inch into the surfaces being joined. In some instances, however, alloying and diffusion can be so extensive as to require special brazing procedures.

Copper alloys very readily with nickel, Monel or the cupro-nickels at furnace temperatures. In this instance molten copper will not flow very far before it picks up enough of the base metal to raise its melting temperature and stop the flow.

Some brazing filler metals, such as aluminum and magnesium brazing filler metals, will alloy and diffuse completely through thin aluminum sheets if held at brazing temperature longer than necessary. Due to excessive diffusion the resulting joint will not be strong and ductile.

Excess molten filler metal which flows by gravity over thin members can erode holes through such thin members by a process of alloying and diffusion.

The brazing of gold to base metals in the production of gold-filled jewelry must be done rapidly in order that the filler metal will not diffuse through the gold and cause discoloration and blemishes.

Wherever excessive alloying and diffusion is liable to occur the brazing should be done in as short a time and at as low a temperature as possible. Sufficient filler metal should be present to fill the joint completely but excess filler metal is both undesirable and uneconomical.

Dissimilar Metal Combinations

Many dissimilar metal combinations may be joined by brazing. In fact, brazing offers solutions to some joining problems when metallurgical incompatibility is the major stumbling block to joining by other welding processes.

There are, however, some limitations. The brazing filler metal must have a melting point below either base metal, and must be compatible with both base metals. Two examples will illustrate this point:

Aluminum brazing filler metals are useful for joining aluminum alloys to themselves but are not satisfactory for joints between aluminum alloys and copper alloys. Silver brazing filler metals are not satisfactory for joining either aluminum or magnesium alloys to themselves or to other metals.

Corrosion Resistance

Corrosion resistance is a subject so complex and requiring so much space that it cannot be covered in this book. Where data are required about the corrosion resistance of a specific metal or about metals to resist specific media, it is best to refer to a standard handbook on the subject such as "The Corrosion Handbook," edited by H. H. Uhlig and published by John Wiley & Sons, Inc., 1948.

Chapter 3

BRAZING FILLER METALS

The American Welding Society defines a brazing filler metal as a metal to be added in making a braze. Brazing filler metals are nonferrous metals or alloys which have melting temperatures above 800 F, but below those of the base metals being joined. Formerly, these metals were referred to as hard solders and brazing alloys but these terms are being replaced by the more clearly defined term *brazing filler metal*.

For satisfactory use as a brazing filler metal, a metal or alloy should have the following properties:

(a) Ability to wet the base metals on which it is used to make a strong, sound bond.

(b) Proper melting temperature and flow properties that permit distribution in properly prepared joints by capillary attraction.

(c) A composition of sufficient homogeneity and stability to minimize separation by liquation under the brazing conditions to be encountered and free of excessively volatile constituents.

(d) Desirable mechanical and physical properties in the joint such as strength, ductility, etc.

Melting of Filler Metals

A better understanding of the nature of brazing filler metals and how to select one for a specific application can be obtained by observing the melting characteristics of metals and alloys. Melting of the pure metals is easy to describe; they transform from the solid to liquid state at one temperature rather than melting over a temperature range. However, the melting of alloys is more complicated. Any series of alloys can best be studied by drawing a chart to show its melting characteristics in relation to chemical composition. Technically, a chart of this type is called a *constitutional diagram*.

Such a diagram is made by preparing a series of alloys that cover the entire range of compositions to be investigated. After careful chemical analysis, cooling curves are made for each alloy from which can be determined the temperature at which the alloy begins to freeze and the temperature at which it becomes completely solid. These points are plotted and connected by lines drawn through them to form a series of curves. It is

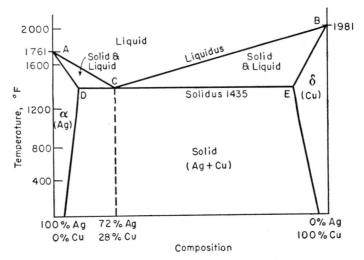

Figure 3.1. Copper-Silver Constitutional Diagram

customary to represent the composition on the horizontal scale and temperature on the vertical scale.

To better illustrate this let us consider the copper-silver constitutional diagram shown in Fig. 3.1.

In order to understand the diagram more fully, the terms used may be defined as follows:

Solidus is the highest temperature at which a metal or alloy is completely solid. (Curve ADCEB of Fig. 3.1.)

Liquidus is the lowest temperature at which a metal or alloy is completely liquid. (ACB of Fig. 3.1.)

Eutectic compositions are those specific alloy compositions that melt at one temperature and not over a range. In this respect, eutectic alloys behave like pure metals. Technically, in the diagram shown in Fig. 3.1, or in any system having a eutectic, the eutectic is that composition where two descending liquidus curves meet and thus the composition at that point has a lower liquidus than its neighboring compositions. (Point C in Fig. 3.1.)

As shown in Fig. 3.1, 100 per cent Ag (Point A) has a melting point of 1761 F. 100 per cent Cu (Point B) has a melting point of 1981 F. The solidus for any composition between 91.2 per cent Ag–8.8 per cent Cu and 8 per cent Ag–92 per cent Cu (Line D E) is 1435 F. From the diagram it can be seen that the eutectic composition is 72 per cent Ag, 28 per cent Cu (Point C). This composition melts and becomes completely liquid at 1435 F. Any composition other than the eutectic composition will not become completely liquid until a higher temperature is reached. For instance, 50 per cent Ag–50 per cent Cu will have a solidus temperature of 1435 F and a liquidus temperature of 1580 F. In other words, this composition of Ag–Cu will begin to melt at 1435 F and will become completely liquid at 1580 F.

The difference between the solidus (ADCEB) and liquidus (ACB) (area bounded by curves ACBECDA) is called the *melting range*. In this range some constituents of the alloy are in the liquid phase and others are in the solid phase.

Melting point and *flow point* are terms which have been in common use, but they have not always been applied with the same meaning and confusion has developed. For this reason the terms *solidus* and *liquidus*, which can be more clearly defined, will be used in this book.

Brazing filler metals with narrow melting ranges (small differences between solidus and liquidus) and eutectic compositions behave during melting and brazing like a pure metal. These brazing filler metals are widely used for brazing in applications where the joint clearance is adequately controlled. They are suitable for processes with either a slow or rapid heating rate.

In contrast to this, there are other brazing filler metals which have wide melting ranges (large differences between solidus and liquidus). Some caution is necessary to avoid too slow heating when using some compositions of this type. When these filler metals are partially melted (above the solidus temperature but below the liquidus temperature) the liquid portion will have a different composition than the solid portion. If this type filler metal is preplaced at the joint and the work brought up slowly through the melting range, then the fluid portion may flow through the joint by capillary attraction leaving a skeletal residue or *skull*. This residue will persist even when heated above the liquidus because the lower melting constituents have already flowed through the joint and are not present to dissolve the higher melting constituents. Separation of the solid and liquid portions in this manner is called *liquation*. If, on the other hand, the work is heated rapidly through the melting range to a temperature above the liquidus, there would be no time for liquation to occur and the filler metal will remain homogenous as it flows through the joint.

The tendency of a filler metal with a wide melting range to liquate is dependent upon the proportions of the alloy that melt and the time when this melting occurs. Compositions that remain virtually solid until high in the melting range may not liquate excessively, while the reverse may be true for compositions part of which become very fluid early in the melting process.

Filler metals with wider melting ranges which do not liquate excessively are frequently an advantage where the fit of parts is not ideal, and especially where uniform clearances cannot consistently be maintained in production. In such an operation when parts have suitable clearances, the filler metal can be applied above its liquidus by capillary attraction. However, when an assembly with excessive clearance is encountered, the filler metal may be applied with care at a temperature within the melting range so that larger gaps can be filled. In the same manner, fillets may be built up which would be impossible without the wide melting range. However, the use of a brazing filler metal in such a manner should be considered an expedient and avoided if possible.

Temperature Required for Brazing

In theory, a brazing filler metal must be completely molten before it can be flowed into a joint and distributed by capillary attraction. Therefore, normally, the liquidus may be considered the lowest temperature which should be used for brazing*, and all sections of the joint must be heated to this temperature or higher. In practice one cannot be sure of heating internal and external sections of an entire joint only to this minimum temperature. The location and rate of heat input, the mass of the parts and the thermal conductivity of the base metals are factors which influence the distribution of heat within the work. With localized rapid heating methods (as induction brazing) temperature distribution is not uniform and the temperature at the heated surfaces will be greater than in inner areas. With slower heating methods (as furnace brazing) where work is heated evenly and slowly, temperature distribution in the assembly is more uniform. (See tables later in this chapter for the recommended brazing temperature range for each brazing filler metal.)

Diffusion and Dilution of Brazing Filler Metal During Brazing

When a brazing filler metal wets the base metal on which it is applied, there may occur a diffusion of the filler metal into the base metal or a dilution of the filler metal by the base metal. Such diffusion and dilution are most apt to occur when the brazing filler metal and the base metal are similar in chemical composition. Factors which may influence the extent of these reactions are (1) the brazing temperature, (2) the length of the brazing cycle, (3) the geometry of the joint being brazed as it affects the area of base metal exposed to the filler metal and (4) the chemical composition of the filler metal. Stress cracking, sometimes referred to as intergranular diffusion of the filler metal, is a localized form of diffusion which is dependent upon stress being present in the base metal. See Chapter 2 for a further discussion of this subject.

Excessive diffusion of a filler metal into the base metal may affect its

---

* There are a few alloys used as brazing filler metals which become substantially liquid below the actual liquidus. With these certain compositions successful brazing can be accomplished even though the liquidus is not attained.

physical and mechanical properties. It is most apt to be serious on thin sections where erosion may produce holes. Dilution of the filler metal alters its liquidus and may result in poor filling of a joint. In order to reduce either diffusion or dilution by a filler metal, the brazing cycle should be kept as short as practical and the brazing temperatures kept low and within the recommended brazing temperature range for the filler metal being used.

Selection of Filler Metal and Brazing Process

The remainder of this chapter is devoted to a discussion of the compositions and uses of the brazing filler metals included in the *Specifications for Brazing Filler Metal* (AWS A5.8-52; ASTM B260 – 52). The compositions shown are nominal. More precise analyses are shown in the Specifications for Brazing Filler Metal. Table 3.1 lists the forms in which the different filler metals are available.

For information on brazing a specific metal or alloy, reference should be made to a later chapter in this book covering that material.

Filler Metals Available

BAlSi (Aluminum-Silicon) Classifications: Brazing filler metals of the BAlSi classifications are used for joining the grades of aluminum alloys shown in Table 12.1 (p. 85).

Correct joint clearance for a particular application is best determined by actual trial. Clearances of 0.006 to 0.010 in. are commonly used for laps less than $\frac{1}{4}$ in. long while clearances up to 0.025 in. are used for longer laps. Torch, dip and furnace brazing processes are most widely used for brazing aluminum although other brazing processes are also employed. The use of flux is essential for all processes. Because of the corrosive nature of these fluxes, the brazed parts must be cleaned thoroughly after brazing. See Chapter 12 for information on removal of fluxes. These filler metals have good resistance to corrosion in most media.

Filler Metal Classification	Nominal Composition			Temperature (°F)		
	Si	Cu	Al	Solidus	Liquidus	Brazing Temperature Range
BAlSi-1	5	—	95	1070	1165	1150–1185
BAlSi-2	7.5	—	92.5	1070	1135	1120–1140
BAlSi-3	10	4	86	970	1085	1060–1185
BAlSi-4	12	—	88	1070	1080	1090–1185

BAlSi-1 brazing filler metal is a general purpose filler metal for torch, dip and furnace brazing.

BAlSi-2 brazing filler metal is available only as a cladding on M1A and

TABLE 3.1. STANDARD FORMS AND SIZES OF BRAZING FILLER METALS

AWS-ASTM Classification	Standard Form	Size, in.
Aluminum-silicon:		
BAlSi-1 and BAlSi-3	Strip	0.020 by 2
	Wire in coils	Round, $\frac{1}{16}$ to $\frac{3}{16}$
	Rod	Round, $\frac{1}{16}$ to $\frac{1}{4}$ by 18 to 36
BAlSi-2	Coated sheet	0.006 to $\frac{1}{4}$[a]
BAlSi-4	Strip	0.020 by 2
	Wire in coils	Round, $\frac{1}{16}$ to $\frac{3}{16}$
Copper-phosphorus:		
BCuP-1	Strip	0.005 to 0.015 by $1\frac{1}{2}$
BCuP-2	Wire in coils	Round, $\frac{1}{16}$ to $\frac{3}{16}$
		Square, $\frac{1}{8}$ to $\frac{3}{16}$
	Rod	Round, $\frac{1}{16}$ to $\frac{1}{4}$ by 18 to 36
		Square, $\frac{1}{8}$ to $\frac{1}{4}$ by 18 to 36
	Powder	50 to 325 mesh
BCuP-3	Wire in coils	Round, 0.047 to $\frac{1}{8}$
	Rod	Round, $\frac{1}{16}$ to $\frac{1}{4}$ by 18 to 36
	Powder	50 to 325 mesh
BCuP-4	Wire in coils	Round, 0.047 to $\frac{3}{16}$
		Square, $\frac{1}{8}$ to $\frac{1}{4}$
	Rod	Round, $\frac{1}{16}$ to $\frac{1}{4}$ by 18 to 36
		Square, $\frac{1}{8}$ to $\frac{1}{4}$ by 18 to 36
	Powder	50 to 325 mesh
BCuP-5	Strip	0.003 to 0.025
	Wire in coils	Round, 0.010 to $\frac{1}{4}$
		Square, $\frac{1}{8}$ to $\frac{1}{4}$
	Rod	Round, $\frac{1}{32}$ to $\frac{1}{4}$ by 18 to 36
		Square, $\frac{1}{8}$ to $\frac{1}{4}$ by 18 to 36
	Powder	50 to 325 mesh
Silver:		
All classifications	Strip	0.003 to 0.025
	Wire in coils	Round, 0.010 to $\frac{3}{16}$
		Square, $\frac{1}{8}$ to $\frac{3}{16}$
	Rod	Round, $\frac{1}{16}$ to $\frac{1}{4}$ by 18 to 36
		Square, $\frac{1}{8}$ to $\frac{1}{4}$ by 18 to 36
	Powder	50 to 325 mesh

TABLE 3.1. (*Continued*)

AWS-ASTM Classification	Standard Form	Size, in.
Copper-gold:		
BCuAu-1 and BCuAu-2......	Strip	To order
	Wire in coils	To order
Copper and copper-zinc:		
BCu, BCuZn-1, BCuZn-2, and	Strip	0.004 to 0.025
BCuZn-3.................	Wire in coils	Round, 0.003 to $\frac{1}{4}$
	Rod	Round, $\frac{1}{16}$ to $\frac{3}{8}$
BCuZn-4....................	Grain	3 to 40 mesh
BCuZn-5....................	Grain	3 to 70 mesh
	Strip	0.006 to 0.025
BCuZn-6...................	Wire in coils	Round, $\frac{1}{16}$ to $\frac{1}{4}$
	Rod	Round, $\frac{1}{32}$ to $\frac{1}{4}$ by 18 to 36
	Strip	0.006 to 0.025
BCuZn-7.................	Wire in coils	Round, $\frac{1}{16}$ to $\frac{1}{4}$
	Rod	Round, $\frac{1}{16}$ to $\frac{1}{4}$ by 18 to 36
	Powder	40 to 180 mesh
Magnesium:		
BMg.......................	Wire in coils	Round, $\frac{3}{64}$ to $\frac{3}{16}$
	Rod	Round, $\frac{3}{64}$ to $\frac{3}{16}$ by 18 to 36
Heat-resisting materials:		
BNiCr.....................	Strip	0.005 to 0.020
	Wire in coils	Round, $\frac{1}{16}$ to $\frac{1}{8}$
	Powder	325 mesh
BAgMn....................	Strip	0.003 to 0.025
	Wire in coils	Round, 0.010 to $\frac{1}{4}$
	Rod	Round, $\frac{1}{16}$ to $\frac{1}{4}$ by 18 to 36

a Coated on one or both sides; coating varies from 5 to 10 per cent of the thickness of the base metal sheet; several aluminum-alloy base metals are available.

J51S aluminum alloy core sheet, coated on one or both sides. It is recommended for dip and furnace brazing.

BAlSi-3 brazing filler metal is a general purpose filler metal for dip and furnace brazing.

BAlSi-4 brazing filler metal is a general purpose filler metal used in some cases for its relatively high corrosion-resistant properties. It is recommended for torch brazing but also may be used for furnace and dip brazing.

BCuP (Copper-Phosphorus) Classifications: Brazing filler metals of the BCuP classifications are used primarily for joining copper and copper alloys with some limited use on silver and molybdenum. Because their phosphorus content will form brittle iron or nickel phosphides, these filler metals are not recommended for ferrous or nickel-bearing metals. They may be applied by all brazing processes and may be used without flux for some applications on copper and silver. However, better results may be expected when a flux is used. Flux is necessary when BCuP filler metals are used with other metals and alloys. Joints made with these filler metals have good electrical and thermal conductivities. Corrosion resistance in most media generally is good. However, they are not recommended for use in sulfurous atmospheres above room temperature.

These filler metals have a tendency to liquate if heated slowly. It is important, therefore, especially if the filler metal is preplaced, to apply heat as rapidly as possible. The color after brazing is light gray. Immersion in 10 per cent sulfuric acid will restore the copper color.

It will be noted in the table below, that the brazing temperature ranges begin below the liquidus. It is a basic principle in brazing that the lowest temperature within the recommended range be used consistent with the joint clearance and the time needed to complete the braze. This in turn will depend on (1) the materials joined, (2) the brazing process employed and (3) the joint design used.

Filler Metal Classification	Nominal Composition			Temperature (°F)		
	Cu	Ag	P	Solidus	Liquidus	Brazing Temperature Range
BCuP-1	95	—	5	1305	1650	1450–1700
BCuP-2	93	—	7	1305	1485	1350–1550
BCuP-3	89	5	6	1195	1500	1300–1550
BCuP-4	87	6	7	1185	1380	1300–1500
BCuP-5	85	15	5	1185	1500	1300–1500

BCuP-1 brazing filler metal is used primarily for preplacing in the joint and is suited particularly for resistance brazing and some furnace brazing applications. This filler metal is somewhat more ductile than the other BCuP filler metals containing more phosphorus and therefore may be made into thin strips. It is also less fluid at brazing temperature than other BCuP filler metals. Joint clearances should be from 0.002 to 0.005 inch.

BCuP-2 brazing filler metal is extremely fluid at brazing temperatures. It will penetrate joints with very little clearance. Best results are obtained with clearances of 0.001 to 0.003 inch.

BCuP-3 brazing filler metal is also extremely fluid at brazing temperatures. Joint clearances of 0.002 to 0.005 in. are recommended.

BCuP-4 brazing filler metal is best used with joint clearances of 0.001 to 0.003 inch.

BCuP-5 brazing filler metal is particularly adaptable where very close fits cannot be held. Joint clearances of 0.003 to 0.005 in. are recommended.

BAg (Silver) Classifications: Brazing filler metals of the BAg classifications are used for joining all ferrous and nonferrous metals except aluminum, magnesium and other metals which have too low a melting temperature. They are used with all brazing processes and are generally free flowing when molten. Joint clearances should be between 0.002 to 0.005 in. for best distribution of the filler metal in the joint by capillary attraction. Flux is generally required. However, for certain processes, particularly with BAg-8, if brazing is done in a vacuum or an inert atmosphere, flux may not be needed.

Filler Metal Classification	Nominal Composition					Temperature (°F)		
	Ag	Cu	Zn	Cd	others	Solidus	Liquidus	Brazing Temperature Range
BAg-1	45	15	16	24	—	1125	1145	1145–1400
BAg-1a*	50	15.5	16.5	18	—	1160	1175	1175–1400
BAg-2	35	26	21	18	—	1125	1295	1295–1550
BAg-3	50	15.5	15.5	16	Ni3	1195	1270	1270–1500
BAg-4	40	30	28	—	Ni2	1240	1435	1435–1650
BAg-5	45	30	25	—	—	1250	1370	1370–1550
BAg-6	50	34	16	—	—	1270	1425	1425–1600
BAg-7	56	22	17	—	Sn5	1145	1205	1205–1400
BAg-8	72	28	—	—	—	1435	1435	1435–1650
BAg-9	65	20	15	—	—	1280	1325	1325–1550
BAg-10	70	20	10	—	—	1335	1390	1390–1600
BAg-11	75	22	3	—	—	1365	1450	1450–1650

* To be added to Specifications for Brazing Filler Metal.

BAg-1 and *1a* brazing filler metals are free flowing and low melting. They are used for general purpose work. Their melting ranges are very narrow. The color after brazing is light yellow.

BAg-2 brazing filler metal is also free flowing and suited for general purpose work at slightly higher brazing temperatures. Its wider melting range is helpful where clearances are not uniform, but care must be taken to prevent liquation. The color after brazing is yellow.

BAg-3 brazing filler metal is used widely for joining carbide tool tips to tool shanks because of its advantage in wetting of the carbide. It has a wide melting range in which the solid and the liquid portions do not tend to separate excessively. This makes it a good filler metal for bridging gaps or forming fillets. It has generally good corrosion-resistant properties but is not as free flowing as BAg-1 and -2. Color after brazing is whitish yellow.

BAg-4 brazing filler metal is, like BAg-3, used extensively for carbide tip brazing although slightly higher brazing temperatures are required. When molten, it flows more freely than BAg-3. The color after brazing is light yellow.

BAg-5 and -6 brazing filler metals are general purpose metals for use with higher brazing temperatures. They may be used where the use of cadmium-containing alloys might be prohibited, as for food handling equipment. The color after brazing is light yellow.

BAg-7 brazing filler metal is a general purpose, low-melting filler metal which does not contain cadmium. It is good for furnace brazing and its whitish color after brazing makes a closer color match with whitish metals like stainless steel. It is used by the dairy and food industries where cadmium-free joints are required. This filler metal has been found to be less prone to cause stress corrosion cracking on stainless steels and some nickel alloys.

BAg-8 brazing filler metal is used where volatile elements are prohibited as in the assembling of vacuum tubes. Although it is free flowing, it does not wet well on ferrous metals. The color after brazing is white.

BAg-9, -10, and -11 brazing filler metals are used particularly for joining sterling silver. These three metals have different brazing temperatures and can be used for step brazing of consecutive joints. The color after brazing is white.

BCuAu (Copper-Gold) Classifications: Brazing filler metals of the BCuAu classifications are primarily used for joining parts in electron tube assemblies where volatile materials are particularly undesirable. In electron tube applications these filler metals are usually used for induction, furnace or resistance brazing in a reducing atmosphere or in a vacuum without flux. For other applications a borax-boric acid flux is used. The two BCuAu filler metals provide a variation in brazing temperature to permit step brazing.

Filler Metal Classification	Nominal Composition		Temperature (°F)		
	Au	Cu	Solidus	Liquidus	Brazing Temperature Range
BCuAu-1	37.5	62.5	1755	1815	1815–2000
BCuAu-2	80	20	1620	1630	1630–1850

BCu and BCuZn (Copper-Zinc) Classifications: Brazing filler metals of the BCu and BCuZn classifications are used for joining various ferrous and nonferrous metals. They can also be used with various brazing processes. Flux is usually necessary except on some furnace brazing operations with a suitable atmosphere. A borax-boric acid flux is common. Joint clearances from 0.002 to 0.005 in. are suitable except for BCu where a press fit to a maximum of 0.002 in. is recommended. With the BCuZn filler metals overheating must be guarded against to prevent volatilization of the zinc content and porous joints. Corrosion resistance of BCuZn filler metals generally differs from the base metals joined and therefore, the service conditions should be taken into consideration when these filler metals are used for joining copper, silicon-bronze, copper-nickel, or stainless steel base metals.

Filler Metal Classification	Nominal Composition			Temperature (°F)		
	Cu	Zn	Others	Solidus	Liquidus	Brazing Temperature Range
BCu	99	—	—	1980	1980	2000–2100
BCuZn-1	60	40	—	1650	1660	1670–1750
BCuZn-2	57	42	Sn 1	1630	1650	1670–1750
BCuZn-3	56	40	Sn 1 Fe 1 Mn 1; Ni 1	1590	1630	1670–1750
BCuZn-4	52.5	47.5	—	1570	1595	1600–1700
BCuZn-5	51.5	45	Sn 3.5	1585	1610	1620–1700
BCuZn-6	48	42	Ni 10	1690	1715	1720–1800
BCuZn-7	47	41.5	Ni 10.5 Ag 1	1685	1710	1690–1800

BCu brazing filler metal is used for joining ferrous metals, nickel and copper-nickel alloys. It is very free-flowing when liquid and widely used, generally without flux for furnace brazing in a hydrogen or dissociated ammonia atmosphere. However, a flux may be required for metals containing such elements as chromium, manganese, silicon, titanium, vanadium, aluminum and zinc, which form oxides that are difficult to reduce.

The oxides of copper in powdered form when subjected to heating in a proper furnace atmosphere, produce a brazed joint essentially similar to joints produced by BCu filler metal.

BCuZn -1, -2, -3, -4, and -5 brazing filler metals are used on steels, copper, copper alloys, nickel, nickel alloys and stainless steel. They are used with the torch, furnace and induction brazing processes.

BCuZn -6 and -7 brazing filler metals, commonly known as white brasses (formerly called nickel silvers), are used with steels, nickel and nickel alloys. They can be used with all brazing processes.

BMg (Magnesium) Classification: Brazing filler metal of the BMg classification is used for joining M1 magnesium base metal. It is used most often with the torch, furnace and dip brazing processes and to some extent with the other brazing processes with the exception of resistance brazing.

Heating must be closely controlled to prevent melting of the base metal. A flux is required with all processes. Clearances from 0.004 to 0.010 in. are best for most applications. Corrosion resistance is good if the flux is removed completely after brazing. For furnace brazing, this filler metal is supplied with a small amount of beryllium which prevents possible ignition. For other brazing processes this addition is not required.

Filler Metal Classification	Nominal Composition			Temperature (°F)		
	Mg	Al	Zn	Solidus	Liquidus	Brazing Temperature Range
BMg	89	9	2	770	1110	1120–1160

BNiCr and BAgMn (Heat-Resistant) Classifications: Brazing filler metal of the *BNiCr* (heat-resistant) classification is used chiefly for joining stainless steels and high nickel alloys to be used at elevated temperatures, such as in the fabrication of jet engines. It also can be used on carbon and low-alloy steels. Joint clearances of 0.002 to 0.005 in. are used. *BNiCr* filler metal retains its heat-resistant properties at temperatures up to 2000 F and also has excellent corrosion-resistant properties. It is used primarily for brazing in a controlled, dry hydrogen atmosphere furnace where no flux is required. It can also be used in a standard controlled atmosphere furnace, but then flux is required.

Brazing filler metal of *BAgMn* heat-resistant classification is used chiefly to join stainless steel and high nickel alloys. It does not have the high temperature strength of the BNiCr filler metal but has good strength in the 500 to 900 F range. Joint clearances of 0.002 to 0.005 in. are used. Furnace brazing with a reducing atmosphere is recommended for best results.

Filler Metal Classification	Nominal Composition	Temperature (°F)		
		Solidus	Liquidus	Brazing Temperature Range
BNiCr	Ni 70; Cr 16.5; Fe + Si + C 10 B 3.5	1850	1950	2000–2150
BAgMn	Ag 85; Mn 15	1760	1780	1780–2100

Chapter 4

FLUXES AND ATMOSPHERES

The purpose of a brazing flux is to promote the formation of a brazed joint. In this sense a gas such as may be used to surround the work and provide an active or protective atmosphere is a flux. For this reason, both fluxes and atmospheres are discussed in this chapter, but to comply with the usual terminology and because the methods of application and characteristics are quite different, fluxes and atmospheres are discussed and tabulated separately.

When metals are exposed to air, chemical reactions occur. The rate of these reactions is generally accelerated as the temperature is raised. The prevalent reaction is oxidation, though nitrides and even carbides are formed in some instances. The rate of oxide formation varies with each metal composition as does the nature of the oxide, i.e., tenacity, structure, resistance to removal, etc. Oxide formation on some metals in air is rapid even at or below room temperatures. In almost all conditions, such oxides or other compounds, if present, prevent the formation of proper brazed joints.

FLUXES

Fluxes are not designed to, nor are they intended for, the primary removal of oxides, oil, grease, dirt or other foreign materials from the parts to be brazed. All parts for brazing must be subjected to appropriate cleaning operations as dictated by the particular metals. See Chapter 7.

In its operation in the making of a braze the flux is needed to combine with, dissolve, inhibit or otherwise render ineffective those unwanted products of the brazing operation which would otherwise impair the braze or totally prevent brazing.

The flux must remain in contact with the braze area to inhibit the further formation of oxides. Since oxides are the principal source of surface contamination it follows that the dissolution and the removal of the oxides during brazing is an important function of a flux. The flux must also be readily displaced by the molten brazing filler metal.

Viscosity of a flux at brazing temperature is an important property in that it influences the ability of the flux to be displaced by the molten filler metal. Another related property is surface tension of the flux; this also affects the wettability of the base metal and the flow of the filler metal into the joint. Under some circumstances flux may be called upon to suppress the volatilization of high-vapor-pressure constituents in a filler metal. These physical characteristics of a flux are also useful, particularly during torch brazing, as a temperature indicator.

When brazing copper with a BCuP type of filler metal, the phosphorus acts as a flux. In this case it is possible to braze without using added flux, but in some cases better results can be obtained if a flux is added.

Chemicals Commonly Used in Fluxes

The following discussion of brazing fluxes is provided for the purpose of enabling the user to understand their function better and thus permit a more effective use of brazing flux. It is not offered with the thought that the user will attempt to formulate his own flux. This is a very complex operation requiring much experience and special equipment.

A very large number of chemical compounds are useful in formulating fluxes. Proprietary fluxes are mixtures of many compounds put together in certain ways that have been found to give satisfactory results for specific purposes. After the chemicals are mixed together (and particularly when they are heated as they are during brazing) reactions take place between the various ingredients. Thus the resulting solution of compounds at brazing temperature is quite different chemically as well as physically from the ingredients which were initially mixed together. For instance, if a fluoborate is an ingredient in a flux, fluorides are formed after the ingredients are mixed even though they have not been added deliberately. During the brazing operation the chemistry is especially transient. The flux, base metals, the filler metals and any gaseous materials that are present react with each other with increasing rapidity as the temperature is raised. The ingredients of the flux must thus be carefully tailored to suit all of the factors in the braze including the time. The flux must not attack the metals too much at the brazing temperature and it must last long enough to enable the joint to be satisfactorily formed. Active halides such as chlorides and fluorides are, for instance, necessary in a flux for aluminum or other highly electropositive metal bearing alloys (see Table 4.1, Types 1, 2, 4 and 6), and some particularly active fluxes need to be mixed just before using to avoid reactions between ingredients during storage.

The following list of chemical compounds includes the most common ingredients of fluxes. Some comments about their functions follow.

Borates (sodium, potassium, lithium, etc.)
Fused borax
Fluoborates (potassium, sodium, etc.)
Fluorides (sodium, potassium, lithium, etc.)

TABLE 4.1. FLUXES FOR BRAZING‡

Important: All materials must be clean before applying flux (see text)

A. W. S. Brazing Flux Type No.	Base Metals on which This Flux is Recommended for Use	Filler Metals on which This Flux is Recommended for Use	Lowest Useful Temperature (°F)	Highest Useful Temperature (°F)	Ingredients (May contain any, some, or all of the classes of compounds listed)	Form as Supplied	Form of Application
1	All brazeable aluminum alloys (See Appendix A)	BAlSi	700	1190	Chlorides Fluorides	Powder	I, II, III, IV
2	All brazeable magnesium alloys (See Appendix A)	BMg	900	1200	Chlorides Fluorides	Powder	III, IV
3	*All except those listed under 1, 2, 4 and 6	All except those listed above	700	2000	Boric acid Borates Fluorides Fluoborates (Must contain fluorine compound) Wetting agent	Powder Paste Liquid	I, II, III
4	†Alloys such as Aluminum-bronze Aluminum-brass containing aluminum additions of 0.5% or more.	BAg, BCuZn, BCuP	1050	1800	Chlorides Fluorides Borates Wetting agent	Paste Powder	I, II, III
5	Same as 3	Same as 3 except note the higher temperature requirement and not recommended for BAg 1 through 7	1000	2200	Borax Boric acid Borates Wetting agent. *No Fluorine in any form*	Powder Paste Liquid	I, II, III
6	Ti and Zr base alloys	BAg	700	1600	Chlorides Fluorides Wetting agent	Paste Powder	I, II, III

* Some Type 3 fluxes are specifically recommended for Base Metals listed under Type 4.

† Combinations of Type 1 and Type 3 fluxes may be used on these materials. In some cases Type 1 is satisfactory.

‡ This table provides a guide for classification of most of the proprietary fluxes available commercially. The information given here is generally not adequate, when used alone, for a specific application.

Chapter 4 should be read thoroughly.

Key to Form of Application:

I. Sprinkle dry powder on joint region.
II. Dip heated filler metal rod in powder or paste.
III. Mix with various vehicles such as water, alcohol, mono-chlorobenzene, or others, to form a paste or slurry.
IV. Molten flux bath.

Chlorides (sodium, potassium, lithium)
Acids (boric; calcined boric acid)
Alkalies (potassium hydroxide, sodium hydroxide)
Wetting agents
Water (either as water of crystallization or as an addition for paste
　　fluxes)

Borates. These compounds are useful in formulating the higher melting fluxes. They have good oxide dissolving power and provide protection against oxidation for long periods of time. Most of the borates melt and are effective at temperatures around 1400 F or higher. Even in the molten condition they have a relatively high viscosity and therefore must be used with other salts.

Fused Borax. Fused borax is another high melting material that is active at high temperatures. However, it is little used in the lower melting brazing fluxes.

Fluoborates. Fluoborates react similarly to the other borates in many respects. However, they do not provide protection from oxidation to the same extent as the other borates. They flow better in the molten state and have greater oxide-dissolving properties than the other borates. Fluoborates are used with other borates or with alkaline compounds, such as carbonates, to make a flux. Another related class of compounds is fluosilicaborates. These are somewhat higher in melting point than the fluoborates and provide good coverage and surface adherence. The high melting point limits their use. (For safety recommendations for fluorine-bearing compounds see Chapter 23.)

Fluorides. The fluorides react readily with most metallic oxides at elevated temperatures and are therefore used in fluxes as cleaning agents. They are particularly important in applications where refractory oxides, like chromium oxides, aluminum oxides, etc. are encountered. In addition to cleaning, the fluorides increase the fluidity of molten borates thereby improving the capillary flow of the molten brazing filler metal. (For safety recommendations for fluorine-bearing compounds see Chapter 23.)

Chlorides. The chlorides function in a manner similar to that of the fluorides. They are less costly but less effective. Chlorides must be used judiciously since, at elevated temperatures, they tend to oxidize the work.

Boric Acid. Boric acid is a principal constituent used in brazing fluxes. It is employed in its conventional form or sometimes in the calcined form. The calcined form reacts similar to boric acid but has a somewhat higher melting point. Boric acid is employed principally as a cleaning agent. However, it is used in a flux because it improves the viscosity of the flux residue. Further, it has the property of facilitating the removal of the glass-like flux residue after brazing. The melting point of boric acid is best described as being below that of the borates but higher than that of the fluorides.

Alkalies. Potassium and sodium hydroxide are used sparingly, if at all, because of their deliquescent properties. Even small amounts involved with other flux agents can create difficulty in humid weather. When used, the function is to elevate the useful working temperature of the flux.

Wetting Agents. Wetting agents are employed in paste and liquid fluxes to facilitate the flow or spreading of the flux onto the work piece prior to brazing. Obviously such wetting agents as are used must not affect adversely the normal functions of the brazing flux.

Water. Water will be present in brazing fluxes either as water of crystallization in the chemicals used in formulating the flux or as a separate addition to the flux for the purpose of making it a paste or liquid. If the water of crystallization is undesirable in a chemical about the only way to remove it is to calcine that particular ingredient. Water which may be used to form a paste must be checked as to its suitability and excessively hard waters should be avoided. In mixing fluxes, if the available water is unsuited, then it is a wise precaution to employ alcohol.

Bases for Choice of Flux

Economic considerations are of course of primary importance. The cost of the flux is outside the scope of this discussion, but it must be kept in mind that the choice and technique of use of flux greatly influence the time required to make a braze and the quality of the braze. There is no single universal flux which is best for all brazing applications. Since there are many variable conditions, i.e., base metal, filler metal, method of brazing, time required to braze, complexity of joint, etc. there are necessarily many useful formulations of flux, each compounded somewhat differently from the other and each having its optimum performance region different from the others. These formulations can, however, be classified into six groups according to their characteristics. Table 4.1 lists these groups with an A. W. S. Brazing Flux Type Number assigned to identify each group. Since the range of functions covered within each group is wide, generally no single flux formulation will best satisfy all of the requirements listed for that Type Number but with few exceptions each flux formulation can be assigned a definite single Type Number and will perform satisfactorily over most of the range stated. Table 4.1 is based on a comprehensive survey of fluxes as reported by their manufacturers. It is offered as a guide to aid in selecting a flux for specific applications and its use will be enhanced when manufacturers state the A. W. S. Type Number in describing their fluxes. Table 4.1 is not a substitute for a thorough search for an optimum flux for a specific high production joint. Recommendations of the supplier should be sought and trial is recommended when experience is lacking. For successful use a flux must be chemically compatible with all of the base metals and filler metals involved in the braze and must be active throughout the brazing temperature range. Knowing the base metals involved and either the temperature at which it is desired to braze or the filler metal which is required, one or more flux types will be found in Table 4.1 for that combination. Where more than one type of flux is recommended, other considerations such as safety (see Chapter 23) and cost will enter into the decision.

Within a particular A. W. S. Type Number of flux, there are several criteria for choosing a specific flux for maximum efficiency:

(1) For dip brazing, water (including water of crystallization) must be avoided.

(2) For resistance brazing, the flux mixture must allow the passage of current.

(3) The effective temperature range of the flux must include the brazing temperature for the specific brazing filler metal involved. This is important both on the high side and the low side of the temperature range. If the time during brazing is long, a less active and longer lived flux is desirable; a quick heating cycle (such as in induction brazing) needs a more active flux and long life is not required. If a nonoxidizing atmosphere is used, the life of the flux is prolonged.

(4) Ease of flux residue removal should be considered.

(5) Corrosive action on the base metal or filler metal should be minimized in the choice of flux.

Methods of Applying Fluxes

Fluxes for brazing are generally available in the form of powder, paste or liquid. The form selected depends upon the individual work requirements, the brazing process and the brazing procedure used.

Frequently, powdered flux is mixed with water or alcohol to make a paste. The powder may also be used in the dry form and sprinkled on the joint, although adherence in this form is not as good. Dry powdered flux may also be applied to the heated end of a filler metal rod simply by dipping filler metal into the flux container. Dry powdered flux is also used in the bath in chemical dip brazing.

Paste is probably the most commonly used form for applying brazing flux. It can be applied to a joint and filler metal before brazing with good adherence. A diluted paste flux is used where the flux is to be sprayed on a joint. Certain flux ingredients will completely dissolve in water to produce a liquid solution which is called "liquid flux" (see Type 3).

The particle size of dry flux or paste flux is sometimes important. Better fluxing action will result when all constituent particles of a flux are small in size and thoroughly mixed. Ball milling or grinding of a flux mixture shortly before use may be helpful.

Liquid flux of Type 5 is used almost exclusively in torch brazing. The fuel gas used is passed through the liquid flux container thus entraining the flux in the fuel gas. With the application of the flame to the work the flux is applied where needed. Usually it is used with a small amount of other flux preplaced and serves to flux the joint surroundings.

Mixtures of powdered filler metal in flux have been successfully used for preplacement of both flux and filler metal.

Flux Removal

Flux residue should be removed to avoid corrosion from active chemicals remaining in it. The residue obtained from a flux, particularly when considerable oxide removal has occurred, is actually a form of glass. The less the flux is required to clean the metal, the less will be the formation of glass and the easier the task of removing the flux residue.

Flux removal from properly cleaned, brazed parts can usually be accomplished by washing in hot water. Thorough drying following this rinse is recommended.

For residues having a moderate amount of glass, removal may be accomplished by immersing the brazed joint in cold water before it has fully cooled down from the brazing temperature. This creates a thermal shock which cracks off the residue. This method should not be used where the thermal cycle involved will impair the strength of the brazed joint.

For residues which are difficult to remove, a chemical dip may be used. See the specific Chapters on base metals for details of pickling solutions and chemical cleaning.

Mechanical methods are used for the removal of flux residues but are usually limited to those cases where any of the above methods will not be effective because of the high glass content. Among the mechanical means used are fiber brush, wire brush, sandblasting, shotblasting, steam jet and chipping with a hammer and chisel. Caution should be exercised to make sure that the method used is compatible with the base metal. Soft metals such as aluminum are susceptible to embedment of flux residue particles.

It should be apparent that the use of an adequate amount of the proper flux will make flux removal easier. Where experience shows that the more difficult methods must be used, use of a greater amount of flux should be considered.

CONTROLLED ATMOSPHERES

Controlled atmospheres are employed to prevent the formation of oxides during brazing and in most cases to reduce the oxides present so that the brazing filler metal can wet and flow on clean base metal.

Like fluxes, controlled atmospheres are not intended primarily for the removal of oxides, grease, oil, dirt or other foreign materials from the parts to be brazed. All parts for brazing must be subjected to appropriate pre-braze cleaning operations as dictated by the particular metals. (see Chapter 7). Controlled atmospheres are most commonly employed in furnace brazing (see Chapter 1). However they may also be used for induction brazing and resistance brazing in special cases. In applications where a controlled atmosphere only is used, the brazed parts are generally ready to use with no necessity for postbraze cleaning. When flux is required, the use of a controlled atmosphere may still be desirable to extend the useful life of a flux and to minimize postbraze cleaning.

The use of controlled atmospheres avoids formation of oxides and scale over the whole part and permits finished machining to be done before brazing in many applications. In some applications, such as electronic tube manufacturing, the elimination of flux is of tremendous importance. Some types of equipment (e.g., metallic muffle furnaces and vacuum systems) may be damaged or contaminated by the use of flux.

Controlled atmosphere brazing is widely used for the production of high quality joints. Large tonnages of assemblies of a wide variety of base metals are mass produced by controlled atmosphere furnace brazing.

Mixtures of some atmospheres with air are explosively combustible within wide temperature ranges. Before heating a furnace retort containing any such atmosphere below 1300 F, it is necessary to purge all air. For example, mixtures of hydrogen with air ranging from 4 to 75 per cent hydrogen are explosive. Waste atmosphere must be either burned or rapidly diluted by adequate ventilation.

The precautions dictated in Chapter 23 should be followed when metals or fluxes containing toxic elements are employed. Some atmospheres contain carbon monoxide (CO) which is toxic. Burning of waste gases or adequate local ventilation are required.

Composition of Atmospheres for Brazing

Table 4.2 lists ten recommended atmosphere types. Approximate compositions are specified for the first seven of these types. The types are listed approximately in the order of increasing difficulty of attainment and maintenance.

The first four brazing atmospheres listed are generated by passing metered mixtures of hydrocarbon fuel gas and air into a retort for reaction.

A.W.S. Brazing Atmosphere Type Number	Source	Maximum Dew Point °F, Incoming Gas	Approximate Composition				Application		Remarks
			%H₂	%N₂	%CO	%CO₂	Filler Metals	Base Metals	
1	Combusted fuel gas (low hydrogen)	Room temp.	.5-1	87	.5-1	11-12	BAg*, BCuZn*, BCuP	Copper, brass*	Decarburizes
2	Combusted fuel gas (decarburizing)	Room temp.	14-15	70-71	9-10	5-6	BCu, BAg*, BCuZn*, BCuP	Copper†, brass*, low-carbon steel, nickel, monel, medium carbon steels§	
3	Combusted fuel gas, dried	-40	15-16	73-75	10-11		Same as 2	Same as 2 plus medium and high-carbon steels, monel, nickel alloys	
4	Combusted fuel gas, dried (carburizing)	-40	38-40	41-45	17-19		Same as 2	Same as 2 plus medium and high-carbon steels	Carburizes
5	Dissociated ammonia	-65	75	25			BAg*, BCuZn*, BCu, BCuP BNiCr	Same as for 1, 2, 3, 4 plus alloys containing chromium‡	
6	Cylinder hydrogen	Room temp.	97-100				Same as 2	Same as 2	Decarburizes
7	Deoxygenated and dried hydrogen	-75	100				Same as 5	Same as 5 plus Co, Cr, W alloys and carbides‡	
8	Heated volatile materials	Inorganic vapors (i.e., zinc, cadmium, lithium, volatile fluorides)					BAg	Brasses	Special purpose. May be used in conjunction with 1 thru 7 to avoid use of flux
9	Purified inert gas	Inert gas (e.g. helium, argon, etc.)					Same as 5	Same as 5 plus titanium, zirconium, hafnium	Special-purpose. Parts must be *very* clean and atmosphere must be pure
10	Vacuum pumping	Vacuum					Any metal which does not vaporize	Any metal which does not vaporize	Special purpose. Elaborate equipment and procedure

* Flux required in addition to atmosphere when alloys which contain volatile components are used.
† Copper should be fully deoxidized or oxygen-free. See Chapters 2 and 14.
‡ Flux must be used in addition to the atmosphere if appreciable quantities of aluminum, titanium, silicon, or beryllium are present.
§ Heating time should be kept a minimum to avoid objectionable decarburization.

With natural gas, the ratio of air to gas may range between 9.5 to 1 and 2 to 1 for the production of useful atmospheres. For mixtures of ratio between 5 to 1 and 9.5 to 1, the reaction is exothermic and the heat liberated is sufficient to continue it. Mixtures richer in natural gas than about 5 (air) to 1 (gas) reqire the addition of heat and the presence of a catalyst in the retort for combustion to take place. This type of reaction is termed endothermic. Mixtures leaner than 9.5 to 1 (less gas) result in a gas product which contains too much molecular oxygen to be suitable for a controlled brazing atmosphere. Following the combustion of such air-gas mixtures, water may be removed either by cooling alone or by the additional use of an absorption type dryer to reduce the dew point to an acceptable value. CO_2 may be scrubbed out if required.

A. W. S. No. 5 brazing atmosphere is obtained by the dissociation of dry ammonia (NH_3) in a catalyst-filled heated retort. Drying of the gas may be necessary if the ammonia is not adequately dry.

The recommended applications for atmospheres are shown in Table 4.2. Recommendations of suppliers of base metals and filler metals should be consulted for specific applications. The atmosphere for brazing must be compatible with both the base metal and the brazing filler metal for satisfactory results, and the equipment used for handling the atmosphere must be such that the atmosphere is applied at brazing temperature without objectionable contamination. The following discussion deals with the action of some of the components of brazing atmospheres:

Hydrogen (H_2). Hydrogen is an active agent for the reduction of most metal oxides at elevated temperatures. However, its presence damages some base metals by hydrogen embrittlement as described in Chapter 2 and in the various sections on specific base metals.

Carbon Monoxide (CO). Carbon monoxide is an active agent for the reduction of some metal oxides, e.g. those of iron, nickel, cobalt, and copper, at elevated temperatures. Carbon monoxide can serve as a desirable source of carbon, as in some applications on carbon steels, or as an undesirable source of carbon and oxygen in other applications. Carbon monoxide can be generated as a contaminent from oil on the parts at brazing temperatures. This gas is toxic. Adequate ventilation must be provided unless waste gas is trapped and burned.

Carbon Dioxide (CO_2). Carbon dioxide serves as an inert diluent of the brazing atmosphere in recommended applications and may provide useful carbon in applications on carbon steels. Its presence may be undesirable as a source of oxygen, carbon and carbon monoxide when decomposed. The carbon dioxide content of the atmosphere can be undesirably increased by air leakage.

Nitrogen (N_2). The presence of nitrogen in a controlled atmosphere is tolerable as an inert diluent in recommended applications. The use of nitrogen must be avoided when the formation of nitrides occurs and is objectionable.

Water Vapor. The tolerable content of water vapor in the atmospheres is specified by the dew point (temperature at which moisture in the gas will condense). Water vapor is undesirable except in applications in which decarburization during brazing is useful. Water vapor may be unintentionally added to the atmosphere from air leakage, air carried into the furnace with the work, free oxygen in the atmosphere, reduction of metal oxides, leakage from water jackets, contaminated gas lines, diffusion of oxygen through inadequate flame curtain, and other less obvious sources. Water vapor is an objectionable source of oxygen in the presence of chromium, zinc, manganese, silicon, aluminum, titanium, magnesium, or beryllium-bearing alloys, where its excessive presence can inhibit wetting by promoting oxidation.

Oxygen (O_2). In addition to sources already mentioned under other components, oxygen may come from air leakage into the furnace, air carried into the furnace with the parts, free oxygen generated in the atmosphere gas, and gases occluded on surfaces in the heating chamber. The presence of oxygen in the brazing atmosphere is always undesirable.

Methane (CH_4). Methane may come from the atmosphere gas as generated or lubricants left on the parts by inadequate cleaning. Methane may also be deliberately added to the gas after it is generated. Methane can serve as a source of carbon and hydrogen.

Inorganic Vapors. In equipment designed for their use, vapors such as those of zinc, cadmium, lithium, and fluorine compounds can serve to reduce metal oxides and scavenge the atmosphere of oxygen. They are useful to replace components of alloys during brazing. These vapors are toxic. (See Chapter 23)

Inert Gases. Inert gases such as helium, argon, and krypton form no compounds with metals. In equipment designed for their use, they inhibit evaporation of volatile components during brazing and permit the use of weaker retorts than are required for a vacuum. Inert gases, as supplied, occasionally contain objectionable water vapor and in such cases should be dried.

Vacuum. By removal of gases to a suitably low pressure (one millionth of atmospheric pressure or less), including gases which are evolved during heating to brazing temperature, very clean surfaces are obtainable. This atmosphere is particularly useful on parts for electronic vacuum tubes, and on metals whose oxides are volatile, unstable, or soluble in the metals at brazing temperature.

In addition to the above components which are mentioned in Table 4.2, the following components may be present unintentionally:

Sulfur (S). Sulfur or compounds of sulfur can react with the metals involved in a braze to inhibit wetting. Sulfur compounds can be introduced from fuel gas used in the generation of the atmosphere, air burned with the fuel gas, lubricants left on surface of the parts as a result of inadequate cleaning, brickwork and other thermal insulation used in the structure of the furnace.

Physical Chemistry of Metal Oxidation

Fig. 4.1* is a graphical presentation of the results of thermodynamic considerations of metal-oxide to gas equilibrium. The ordinate is the logarithm of the ratio of water vapor partial pressure to hydrogen partial pressure; the abscissa is the reciprocal of the absolute temperature, with the temperature in Fahrenheit degrees also indicated. The lines drawn for each oxide represent equilibrium conditions of metal and metal oxide. Below these lines are conditions of temperature and dew point wherein the oxide may be reduced by hydrogen. Above these lines, water vapor may oxidize the metal in question.

From Fig. 4.1, the effect of dew point on the metal oxide equilibrium is evident for manganese, chromium, and silicon. For example, chromium oxide (Cr_2O_3) is in equilibrium with hydrogen gas having a dew point of 0 F when the material is at approximately 3000 F; with a −50 F dew point hydrogen at about 2300 F; and with a −100 F dew point hydrogen at about 1750 F. If chromium oxide is to be reduced and thus present a clean metallic surface suitable for brazing, the dew point of the hydrogen must be below these equilibrium values at brazing temperature. The effectiveness of A. W. S. atmospheres No. 2 and No. 4 are also shown for specified ratios of partial pressures of CO_2 to CO. It is apparent that dry hydrogen is a much more effective reducing agent than carbon monoxide.

Such curves aid in comprehending the actions of hydrogen and water vapor in respectively reducing and oxidizing metal oxides and metals, but they do not portray the complete story involved in the use of controlled atmospheres. They do not indicate the rate at which reduction will occur nor the physical form of the oxide. The curves show whether the removal of these oxides for the assumed chemical reaction is possible under the conditions of gas composition and temperature indicated. In each case, the oxide is assumed to be reduced to the metal in one operation, which may not be the case.

It is also possible that complex metal oxides may not behave in a manner

---

* From Armour Research Foundation of Illinois Institute of Technology Final Report: *Literature Review and Industrial Survey of Brazing*, Project No. 90-1060B for Frankford Arsenal.

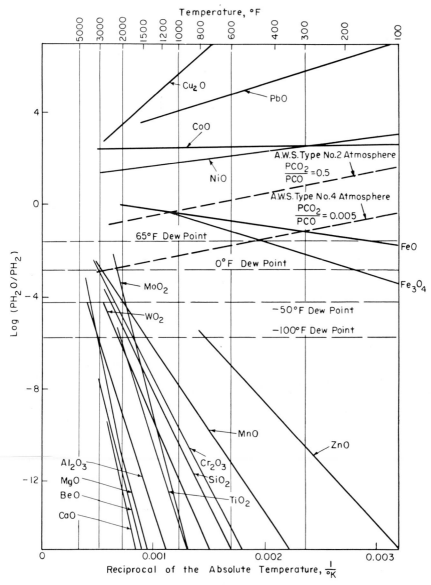

Figure 4.1. Equilibrium relationships in controlled atmospheres

similar to simple oxides. It will be noted that oxides of aluminum, magnesium, beryllium, calcium and titanium are only reducible at very high temperatures and with very low dew points. Usually the equilibrium temperature is far above a useful temperature for brazing. If a base metal contains small amounts of those elements (below 0.5 per cent), a satisfactory braze can usually be obtained. If greater amounts of these elements are present in the base metal, a flux must be used or a surface plating employed to mask the unreducible oxides.

The predictions of Fig. 4.1 are in rough agreement with actual observations. A notable deviation is that copper oxidizes between 150 F and 350 F even in a hydrogen atmosphere having a dew point below 0 F. It should be borne in mind that experiments in brazing with a controlled atmosphere are subject to considerable error unless extreme precautions are taken to avoid contamination of the atmosphere. Some of the contaminations which are apt to occur are pointed out in this Chapter under *composition of atmospheres*. Other experimental difficulties include that of the analysis of the atmosphere gas at brazing temperature in the immediate vicinity of the brazing operation.

A rigorous theoretical treatment would include reaction rates—not only the reaction of the reducing gas with the metal oxide but all other possible reactions such as metal with oxide and metal with atmosphere, as well as effects due to unstable oxides. The influences of alloying elements further complicate the problem on commercially available metals. When solutions to these problems are known, it will be possible to predict the controlled atmosphere requirement for each brazing application. Meanwhile, recommendations of suppliers of materials and equipment should be sought when difficulties are encountered or development of maximum efficiency high production is justified.

Many combinations of base metals and brazing filler metals can be used for the efficient production of brazed joints using suitable standard controlled atmospheres in lieu of flux without such precise control of the atmosphere as may seem to be implied by explaining potential sources of difficulty.

Bases for Choice of Atmosphere

In general, the atmosphere listed nearest the top of Table 4.2 for recommended application to the specific base metals and filler metal involved in the braze should be selected. The footnotes associated with the table are important, and these points are elaborated in the discussion of *composition of atmospheres*. When base metals susceptible to carburization or decarburization (see Chapters 15, 16 and 17) are to be heated in the atmosphere to temperatures at which these reactions take place, an atmosphere compatible to this requirement must be chosen. In applications involving metals which may be embrittled (see Chapters 2 and 14) by hydrogen or which may combine chemically with hydrogen (e.g., tantalum), the amount of hydrogen present in the atmosphere must be kept below a suitable maximum value.

Probably the most widely employed (on a tonnage basis) controlled atmosphere brazing is the use of BCu on steel with A. W. S. Numbers 1, 2, 3, 5 or 6 atmospheres being employed, depending upon the composition and requirements imposed upon the steel.

Chapter 5
DRAFTING ROOM PRACTICES

As with any other industrial fabricating process, it is important that brazed joints be properly engineered. It is the function of the engineer to design the joint so that it will withstand the service conditions to which the finished fabrication will be exposed.

At the same time, the joint should be so disposed that it can be made without inconvenience and, insofar as possible, with existing shop facilities. For this reason a close cooperation between shop and engineering personnel cannot be over-emphasized.

The designer can best convey his design to the fabricating department by use of the Standard Welding Symbols of the American Welding Society. These symbols provide a means for identifying the brazing procedure to be used as shown in Fig. 5.1. If necessary, supplementary sketches and notes should be included on the design drawings to show details of the joint preparation and configuration.

It is strongly recommended that the designer familiarize himself with the other chapters in this book so that he will fully appreciate and give due consideration in his design to such matters as assembly, filler metal feed, and the selection of the brazing process.

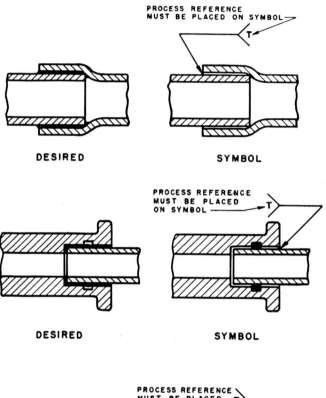

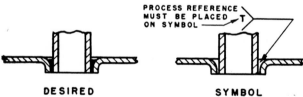

Figure 5.1. Application of brazing symbols

Chapter 6

JOINT DESIGN

The design of a joint to be brazed is dependent on a number of factors, the most important of which are:

Selection of base metals and filler metal

Types of joint

Service requirements

Mechanical strength

Electrical conductivity

Pressure tightness

Performance at elevated and sub-zero service temperatures

The following discussion of joint design is fundamental in nature and will be applicable for most of the generally used base metals and classes of brazing filler metals.

Selection of Base Metals and Filler Metals

It is assumed that the designer has a basic knowledge of the part or assembly to be designed and its intended functions. From this information the base metal that will best suit the application is determined.

There are usually one or more filler metals which are applicable for brazing any of the commonly used base metals. Table 6.1 shows base metals indexed against each other to give the recommended filler metals for similar and dissimilar metals.

Sometimes more than one filler metal may be selected for a given assembly to permit brazing adjacent to a previously-made joint without disturbing the previous joint. A brazing filler metal with a high melting range is selected for the first joint and successively lower range filler metals are selected for subsequent joints. This practice is commonly called *step brazing*.

A note of caution is in order at this point. Where base metals having different coefficients of thermal expansion are to be brazed, care must be taken not to introduce stress that can cause failure of the base metal or joint during or after brazing.

Types of Joints

The selection of a joint design for a specific application will depend largely upon the service requirements of the assembly but may also depend upon

TABLE 6.1. BASE METALS VS. FILLER METALS

(Similar and Dissimilar Combinations)

Base Metal	Aluminum and Aluminum Alloys	Magnesium and Magnesium Alloys	Nickel and Nickel Alloys	Carbon and Low-Alloy Steels	Stainless Steels	Irons	Copper and Copper Alloys	High Carbon and Tool Steels	Heat-Resistant Alloys
Al and Al alloys	BAlSi								
Mg and Mg alloys	x	BMg							
Ni and Ni alloys	x	x	BAg, BCu, BNiCr						
Carbon and low-alloy steels	BAlSi-4	x	BAg, BCu, BCuZn, BNiCr	BAg, BCu, BCuZn, BNiCr					
Stainless steels	x	x	BAg, BCu, BCuZn, BNiCr	BAg, BCu, BCuZn, BNiCr	BAg, BCu, BCuZn, BNiCr				
Irons	x	x	BAg, BCu, BCuZn	BAg, BCu, BCuZn	BAg, BCu, BCuZn	BAg, BCu, BCuZn			
Copper and copper alloys	x	x	BAg, BCuZn	BAg, BCuZn	BAg, BCuZn	BAg, BCuZn	BAg, BCuP, BCuZn		
High carbon and tool steels	x	x	BAg, BCu, BCuZn	BAg, BCu, BCuZn	BAg, BCu, BCuZn	BAg, BCu, BCuZn	BAg, BCuZn	BAg, BCu, BCuZn	
Heat-resistant alloys	x	x	BAg, BCu, BCuZn, BNiCr	BAg, BCu, BCuZn, BNiCr	BAg, BCu, BCuZn, BAgMn, BNiCr	BAg, BCu, BCuZn, BNiCr	BAg, BCuZn,	BAg, BCu, BCuZn,	BAg, BCu, BCuZn, BAgMn, BNiCr

For more complete details on the properties and limitations of base metals refer to Chapters 12 through 22.
For operating characteristics and usability of brazing filler metals refer to Chapter 3.
x = not recommended.

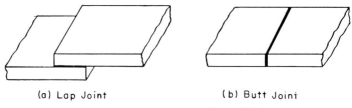

(a) Lap Joint   (b) Butt Joint

Figure 6.1. Basic types of brazed joints

such factors as the brazing process to be employed, fabrication techniques prior to brazing, quantities to be brazed, method of applying filler metal, and others. When the service requirements of a joint are severe it generally means that the load-carrying capacity of the joint should equal or exceed the load-carrying capacity of the weakest member of the assembly.

The mechanical properties of a brazing filler metal in a joint seldom match the mechanical properties of the base metals being joined. The unit strength of the filler metal occasionally is higher than that of the base metal but usually it is considerably lower. The unit strength of the joint is also affected by the joint clearance, as will be explained later, and by the presence of defects such as porosity, flux inclusions and unbrazed areas or voids.

There are only two basic types of joint design used for brazing. These two are the lap joint illustrated in Fig. 6.1 (a) and the butt joint illustrated in Fig. 6.1 (b). There are, however, many combinations and variations of lap and butt joints used in brazing applications.

In the lap joint (Fig. 6.1 a) the area of overlap may be varied so that the joint will be as strong as the weakest member despite the lower unit strength of the filler metal or the presence of small defects in the joint. An overlap greater than three times the thickness of the thinnest member will usually yield maximum joint efficiency.

Lap joints should be employed wherever possible, since they offer the greatest possibility of obtaining joints with maximum efficiency. They do have the disadvantage of increasing the metal thickness at the joint.

Butt joints (Fig. 6.1 b) are limited in joint area to the cross-sectional area of one member. If a high joint efficiency is to be obtained, the braze must be free of defects. With butt joints it is difficult to fulfill this requirement in most applications. Therefore, they should only be used where service requirements are not severe and where leak tightness and strength are relatively unimportant.

Scarf joints (Fig. 6.2) are a variation of the butt joint used to increase the joint area. The use of the scarf joint is somewhat questionable unless the joint area obtained thereby is over three times the normal cross-sectional area. Scarf joints are more difficult to prepare and harder to hold in align-

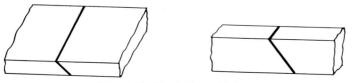

Figure 6.2. Typical scarf joints

ment during brazing than are lap or butt joints. Tee joints and corner joints are considered to be butt joints.

Service Requirements

Mechanical Strength. A joint may be subjected to various types of stresses such as tension, compression, shear, impact and fatigue. The effect of different factors on the mechanical strength of brazed joints is discussed in this section.

Joint Clearance Vs. Mechanical Strength. Joint clearance has a direct bearing on the mechanical strength of any brazed joint no matter how it is stressed. It has been proven that joint clearance with its effect on the subsequent thickness of brazing filler metal in the joint is a determining factor in obtaining the maximum strength for a given design.

In this discussion *clearance* is the dimension between the interfaces of the completed brazed joint. However, clearance between the brazed parts must be considered in terms of conditions at one specific instant, i.e., room temperature or brazing temperature. With similar metals of about equal mass, the room temperature clearance (before brazing) is a satisfactory guide. In brazing two dissimilar metals, the one with the higher thermal expansion may tend to close up or widen the clearance depending upon the relative positions and configurations of the base metals. Thus when brazing dissimilar metals (or greatly differing masses of similar metals) consideration must be given to the clearance at brazing temperature and adjustments made in the room temperature clearance to achieve the desired clearance at brazing temperature.

A convenient index of brazing temperature clearance is the thickness of the braze in the finished joint, provided there has not been appreciable diffusion during brazing. This thickness can be measured on a section of the joint.

As an illustration of the influence of joint clearance (as measured on completed brazed joints) consider a brazed joint of carbon steel to carbon steel as shown in Fig. 6.3. This shows a plot of shear strength vs. joint clearance for joints made with BAg-1 filler metal and flux.

The curve may be more or less pronounced than shown in Fig. 6.3. However, it has been generally accepted that for each particular brazing filler

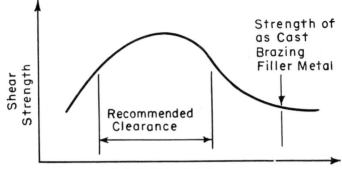

Figure 6.3. Shear strength vs. joint clearance (Brazing low-carbon steel with silver alloy filler metal).

TABLE 6.2. RECOMMENDED JOINT CLEARANCES AT BRAZING TEMPERATURE

Filler Metal AWS-ASTM Classifications	Joint Clearance (in.)*
BAlSi Group	0.006–0.010 for length of lap less than ¼ in.
	0.010–0.025 for length of lap greater than ¼ in.
BCuP Group	0.001–0.005
BAg Group	0.002–0.005
BCuAu Group	0.002–0.005
BCu	0.000 to 0.002†
BCuZn Group	0.002–0.005
BMg	0.004–0.010
BNiCr	0.002–0.005
BAgMn	0.002–0.005

* In the case of round or tubular members this means a clearance on the radius.
† For maximum strength use 0.000 clearance or a press fit.

metal and base metal combination there is an optimum clearance range which will give the best joints.

Table 6.2 may be used as a guide in designing for maximum joint strength. If clearances are used which are less than those recommended, the joint strength may fall appreciably due to excessive voids, flux inclusions, etc. Larger clearances will permit greater flexibility in machining but may result in weaker joints and waste filler metal.

The joint clearances shown in Table 6.2 should be maintained at brazing temperature. Clearances at room temperature should include allowance for expansion at the higher temperature of brazing.

When brazing dissimilar metals it is advisable to check their coefficients of thermal expansion, especially in the brazing temperature range, since a number of difficulties may arise. Two of these are:

(1) Where one part fits inside another, the expansion of the inner

part may be such that when the brazing temperature is reached there will be a metal-to-metal contact. Thus the proper clearances (Table 6.2) will not be maintained and little, if any, brazing filler metal will enter the joint and only a fillet will be formed. Transposing the metal parts may produce the opposite condition, increasing the clearances, and may prevent capillary attraction.

(2) Assuming the brazing filler metal does enter the joint, a greater contraction of the inner part can result in fraction of the filler metal in the joint during cooling.

Stress Distribution. Figure 6.4 shows typical joints which may be used

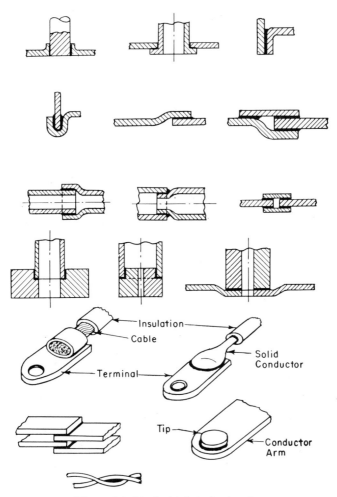

Figure 6.4. Typical joints for brazing

where normal mechanical strength is required. It must be remembered
that, wherever possible, lap joints are preferred. Butt and scarf joints
should be used only where lap joints cannot be tolerated because of space
limitations.

The design of a joint should be such as to avoid stress concentrations
that cause tearing. This can frequently be done by imparting flexibility

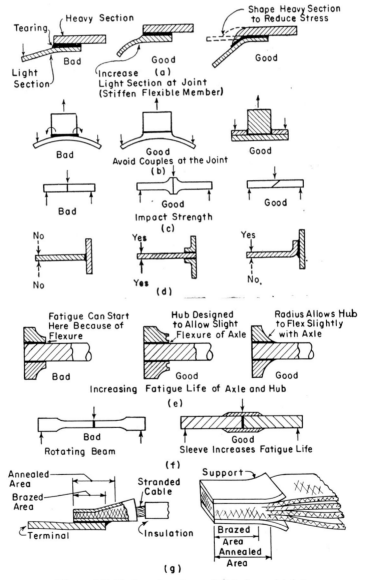

Figure 6.5. Preferred and unsuitable brazed joints

ʻreduced rigidity) to that part of the assembly where joint failure is apt to start. Alternatively, the flexible part may be stiffened at the joint. Figure 6.5 illustrates correct and incorrect designs for the types of loading shown.

Note in Fig. 6.5 (g) that for applications where vibration or fatigue is a factor, the parts should be supported mechanically beyond the brazed joint and annealed base metal.

Face Feeding and Preplacement of Brazing Filler Metal. An important part of joint design is the manner in which the filler metal will be introduced into the joint. Therefore the designer must know what brazing process will be used or he must decide what processes can be employed.

Normally, where joints are being brazed manually, the brazing filler metal is face fed and little or no problem exists. However, where there is enough production to warrant the use of machine or automatic equipment for brazing, or where a special problem exists preplacement of the brazing filler metal may be required. This must be taken into account in the design of the joint.

The brazing filler metal may be preplaced in the form of wire, shims, strip, powder, etc. Of these, wire and strip are perhaps most generally used. Some brazing filler metals may also be preplaced by a spraying procedure similar to that used in metallizing.

Fig. 6.6 illustrates a number of ways in which wire may be preplaced.

Note that in cases where a groove is cut in the base metal for preplacing wire such as in Figs. 6.6 (b) and (c) the heavier section is grooved in each case.

The brazing filler metal flows from the groove and is distributed throughout the joint as shown in Fig. 6.7. Thus it is essential to subtract the grooved area from the joint area in designing for mechanical strength.

In the design of joints where preplaced shims or thin flat sections of brazing filler metal are to be used it is important that the parts be free to move as the brazing filler metal shim melts. In this way, excess filler metal and flux is squeezed out of the joint by the proper application of pressure during the brazing cycle (see Fig. 6.8).

Electrical Conductivity. The principal factor to be considered in the

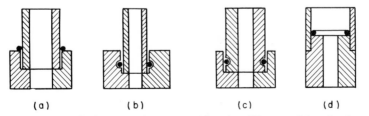

(a)   (b)   (c)   (d)

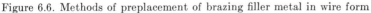

Figure 6.6. Methods of preplacement of brazing filler metal in wire form

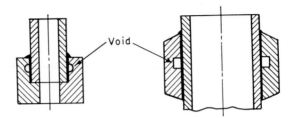

Figure 6.7. Brazed joints with grooves for preplacement of filler metal

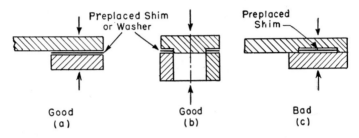

Figure 6.8. Preplacement of brazing filler metal in shim form

design of an electrical joint is electrical conductivity. The joint, when properly designed, should not add appreciable electrical resistance to the circuit.

It is recognized that brazing filler metals in general have very low electrical conductivity as compared to copper. As an example BCuP-5 filler metal has approximately 10 per cent the conductivity of copper and BAg-6 filler metal 24.4 per cent the conductivity of copper. A brazed joint will not add any appreciable resistance to the circuit provided the recommended joint clearances shown in Table 6.2 are used. The shorter path through the brazing filler metal as compared to the longer path through the conductor results in only a negligible increase in the total resistance in the circuit.

As an illustration consider the extreme case shown in Fig. 6.9. This figure shows a copper conductor of one square inch cross section containing

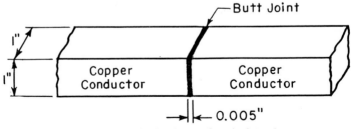

Figure 6.9. Brazed joint in an electrical conductor

a joint brazed with BCuP-5 brazing filler metal using an 0.005 in. joint clearance as recommended in Table 6.2.

R_{Cu} = Resistance of copper = 6.79 $\times$ 10^{-7} ohms/in./in.^{2}
IACS at 20°C

$$R_{FM} = \text{Resistance of filler metal} = \left(\frac{1}{C_{FM}}\right) R_{Cu}$$

Where C_{FM} = conductivity of filler metal = approx. 10% for BCuP-5

Therefore,

$$R_{FM} = \left(\frac{1}{0.10}\right) 6.79 \times 10^{-7} = 67.9 \times 10^{-7} \text{ ohms/in./in.}^2$$

l = Joint clearance = Electrical path = 0.005 in. for BCuP-5 through joint

Let L = Length of copper conductor + length brazed butt joint assume L = 1.000 in.

Then total resistance = $R_T = (L\text{-}l) R_{Cu} + 1R_{FM}$

$$R_T = (0.995)\, 6.79 \times 10^{-7} + (0.005)\, 67.9 \times 10^{-7}$$

$$R_T = 7.10 \times 10^{-7} \text{ ohms/in./in.}^2$$

Per cent resistance raised by butt joint in 1 in. of conductor

$$= \frac{R_T - R_{Cu}}{R_{Cu}} \times 100 = 4\tfrac{1}{2}\%$$

As the length of the conductor increases the influence of the brazed joint decreases. Thus if the length of conductor were 2 in. instead of 1 in. the increase in electrical resistance would be $2\tfrac{1}{4}$ per cent.

From a practical standpoint it must be recognized that there will be a certain amount of voids which will cut the effective area of the electrical path. For this reason lap joints are recommended where design will permit.

A lap length of $1\tfrac{1}{2}$ times the thickness of the thinner member of the joint will give a resistance approximately equal to the same length in solid copper (see Fig. 6.10). This is a rule of thumb which has been used extensively with good results. A longer lap may be used as necessary for convenience or for some special reason.

Pressure Tightness. Joints in pressure-tight assemblies should be of the lap (shear) type whenever possible. This not only provides the strongest type of joint but also provides a larger brazed area (interface) with less chance for leaks through the joint. Fig. 6.11 illustrates a few examples.

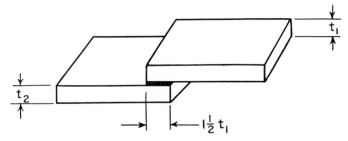

Figure 6.10. Optimum lap for joints—electrical conductors

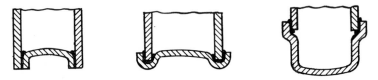

Figure 6.11. Typical brazed joints for pressure-tight containers

The principal factor other than strength to be considered in the design of pressure or vacuum-tight assemblies is the importance of proper venting.

The heat from the brazing operation expands the air or gases within a closed assembly so rapidly that unless the assembly is well vented (open to the atmosphere) it is likely to be forced apart. At the same time, forces may act on the filler metal entering and flowing through the joint and tend to minimize the effect of capillary attraction (see Fig. 6.12).

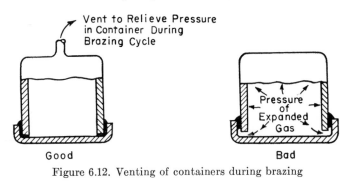

Figure 6.12. Venting of containers during brazing

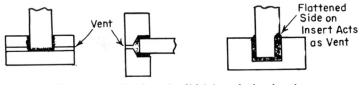

Figure 6.13. Venting of solid joints during brazing

Dead-end holes may be considered as small pressure containers. Fig. 6.13 illustrates a means of designing a joint with vents to eliminate the build-up of pressure during the brazing cycle.

Elevated Temperature Service. It can readily be understood that rules as to the maximum operating temperatures that a brazed assembly will stand are necessarily complex when so many filler metals and base metals are involved. This, coupled with the fact that maximum temperatures may be involved for a relatively long or short duration, is why the subject can only be treated in a very general manner.

All metals and alloys lose strength as the temperature increases. Brazing filler metals are no exception. Therefore, brazed joints can be expected to lose strength as temperature increases.

Unfortunately, there are little short time tensile test data and still less creep and stress rupture test data available on brazed joints at elevated temperatures. Where a contemplated design involves brazing for elevated temperature service, the design must take into account the lowered load-carrying capacity of the joint. Sample joints tested under actual service conditions are the only safe method or predicting service life.

Table 6.3 lists the suggested maximum service temperatures for various brazing filler metals. It will be noted that two such temperatures are suggested based upon different concepts of design. Environment, stress and time as well as temperature must be considered when selecting a brazing filler metal for a specific application just as the same factors must be considered in the selection of the base metals. Where stress and time will permit, the suggested maximum service temperatures are applicable.

TABLE 6.3

Filler Metal, AWS-ASTM Classification	Suggested Limiting Service Temp. for Continuous Service (F)	Suggested Max. Service Temp., (F)
BCuP Group	300	300
BAg Group	400	500
BCuZn Group	400	500
BCU	400	900
BAgMn	500	900
BNiCr	1000	2000

Sub-zero Service Temperatures. Present data indicate that the tensile, shear and impact properties of brazed joints are not adversely affected by low service temperatures, at least to -100 F. When in doubt, samples should be tested to determine whether or not the necessary requirements of time, temperature and strength can be met by the joint at the intended service temperature.

Chapter 7

PRECLEANING AND SURFACE PREPARATION

A clean, oxide-free surface is imperative to insure uniform quality and a sound brazed joint. If all grease, oil, dirt and oxides have been carefully removed from the filler metal and base metal before brazing, there is a much better chance of obtaining a sound joint because only then can uniform capillary attraction be obtained. Even though many fluxes do have some cleaning effect this is not their primary function.

Fluxes are used primarily to prevent the formation of oxides during brazing, to reduce the surface tension of the filler metal and to form a protective covering of slag over the solidifying brazed joint. Their effectiveness in removing existing oxides is only slight and incidental.

It is recommended that brazing be done as soon as possible after the material has been cleaned. The time the cleaning remains effective depends on the metals involved, atmospheric conditions, storage, handling, etc.

Cleaning is commonly divided into two major categories, chemical and mechanical. Because it is most effective, chemical cleaning is usually used to remove all traces of oil or grease. Carbon tetrachloride, trichlorethylene, and trisodium phosphate are the usual cleaning agents employed. See Chapter 23 for safe use of these cleaners.

Other chemical means are required to remove various types of oxides and scales which cannot be accomplished by the use of the above-mentioned cleaners. Many commercial products are on the market to achieve this purpose. The choice of any one cleaner will depend on the individual application. Whichever cleaner is used it is very important that all residue be removed from the metal by careful rinsing since it may attack the base metal or form another equally undesirable film on the surface.

Objectionable surface conditions can also be removed by mechanical means such as grinding, filing, scratch brushing or any form of machining provided joint clearances are not disturbed. However, if kerosene or oils were used in machining, they must be removed prior to brazing.

Use of brazing for repair of broken parts, tools, etc. requires thorough removal of paint, lacquer or any other coating that may be present.

For information on the cleaning of a specific metal see the chapter covering that metal.

Chapter 8

ASSEMBLY

The method of assembling parts to be brazed should be selected at the time the parts are designed and the brazing process and type of joint to be used should be determined at the same time since all these factors are closely related. As a general rule it is desirable to employ the simplest method of assembly which will securely hold the parts to be brazed in their correct alignment during the heating and cooling cycle of the brazing operation. In many instances it is possible to design the parts so that they may be assembled and brazed without the use of fixtures, while in other cases it may be advisable or necessary to provide clamps and supports to insure that the parts are firmly held in correct alignment.

Many methods are employed to assemble parts for brazing without the use of auxiliary fixtures. Some of these are listed below and some are also illustrated in Fig. 8.1:

By gravity, employing the weight of the parts alone or aided by additional weights.

By tack welding the assembly at points with either spot, projection or arc welds.

By spinning operations.

By crimping operations

By interlocking seams.

By swaging operations.

By expanding, such as the ends of tubes into a header plate.

By peening.

By screws.

By rivets.

By pinning using either straight or tapered pins.

By staking operations.

By dimpling operations.

By bumping operations.

By use of shoulders fabricated on one of the parts.

By interference, press of knurled fits if assembly is to be copper brazed in a furnace, since no joint allowance is needed in design for flow of the filler metal.

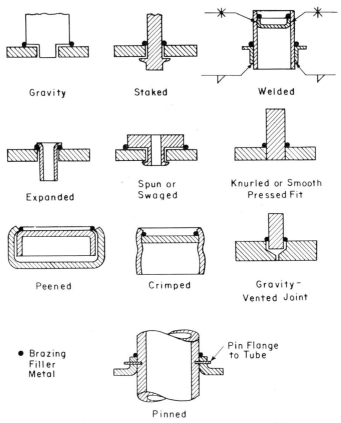

Figure 8.1. Typical self-jigging brazing assemblies

Where fixtures are employed for assembling parts for brazing, consideration should be given to the following factors:

The mass of the fixture should be kept to the minimum that will adequately accomplish its purpose. The fixture must be designed so that it will not interfere with the even heating of the parts being brazed by removing heat through conduction from the brazing area, or hamper the flow of the brazing filler metal.

The material from which the fixture is made must be selected with consideration of the brazing process to be used. Furnace brazing for example requires the use of materials which will withstand the temperatures involved without appreciably weakening or distorting.

Consideration must be given to the expansion and contraction of the fixture in relation to the parts being brazed to assure a combination which will maintain the proper joint clearance and alignment *at the brazing tem-*

perature. This involves consideration of the coefficient of expansion of the fixture material as related to that of the material from which the assembled parts are made.

The fixture should be made of material which will not readily alloy at elevated temperatures with the material of the assembled parts where they come in contact and it should be designed so that it will not be wet by the brazing filler metal.

There are certain other requirements for brazing fixtures which are peculiar to the particular brazing process selected.

In torch brazing, for example, the fixture must allow free access to the joint to be brazed for application of the torch flame as well as the brazing filler metal.

In furnace brazing the fixtures must withstand the heat of the furnace during the brazing cycle. Lever systems, cams or weights are used extensively for maintaining pressure on assembled parts during heating and cooling; springs are seldom employed because of the loss of tension upon heating.

Fixtures for induction brazing also present a problem since it is desirable to keep all metal except the assembly being brazed away from the field of the induction coil. Fixtures made from porcelain, mica, ceramics or asbestos are of advantage in such instances.

Other brazing processes present similar individual problems which must be considered along with the fundamental jigging requirements that the assembled parts be held in correct relationship regardless of the expansions and contractions during the brazing cycle; that even heating of the assembled parts be obtained despite differences in the mass of the parts and the fixture; and that there is no interference with the free flow of the brazing filler metal into the joint.

It is frequently advisable to design a fixture to serve as a heat shield or heat absorber as well as a positioning fixture.

Chapter 9

TECHNIQUE OF BRAZING

The results obtained in brazing depend largely upon proper joint design, cleanliness, jigging and the use of suitable fluxes and filler metal. Incorrect brazing techniques can cause inferior results regardless of sound engineering. It is advisable to bring the joint to brazing temperature in as short a time cycle as possible, but this must be done in a manner to prevent general underheating, localized overheating and the development of high thermal stresses.

Preheating is considered to be any preliminary heat application given to an assembly prior to the brazing cycle. For instance, in torch brazing, the initial heat application given particularly to heavy parts or parts of different thicknesses is considered preheating even though it is part of the brazing cycle. Preheating is used to minimize thermal shock and temperature gradients and to prevent cracking.

Torch Brazing

The production of satisfactory joints by torch brazing requires skill on the part of the brazer. Generally, a slightly reducing flame is desirable. The adjustment of the oxy-acetylene flame is relatively simple and may be maintained by observing the characteristics of the flame. The proper adjustment of flames of other types of fuel gases is more difficult as no marked visual change in flame characteristics takes place. The adjustment can be made and controlled by the use of flow meters or gas analysis. The outer envelope of the flame, not the inner cone, should be applied to the work. This is mentioned because this technique is different from that used in gas welding.

Torch preheating of adjacent members will depend upon the size, shape and thermal conductivity of the metals and the type of joint. Improper heating, primarily due to poor manipulation of the torch, may cause cracking, excessive diffusion and/or oxidation of the brazing filler metal, as well as incomplete joint penetration.

In addition to proper heating to offset high thermal conductivity of joint members and stress cracking due to thermal shock, it is important that the joint be brought to such a uniform temperature within the brazing temperature range that the filler metal flows freely and fills the joint. Overheating must be avoided and this is best accomplished by using an active flux with a melting point not too far below the brazing temperature range of the filler metal. The melting of the flux can then serve as an indicator of the approach to the proper brazing temperature. If the brazing filler metal is to be face fed, it is touched to the joint as heating progresses until it melts and flows freely through the joint. Then heating is stopped. This technique makes the joint area itself in effect "a soldering iron" and overheating is avoided. It is poor practice to apply the torch flame directly to the filler metal or flux for the purpose of melting or flowing.

It is advisable to maintain a fairly uniform temperature at the joint. To accomplish this, auxiliary or multiple tip or multi-flame torches may be necessary. In mechanized operations, the parts can be moved, oscillated or rotated as they pass through the heating zone. Alternatively, the flames are moved around the parts. In some operations, torches or burners are so disposed as to heat the parts over the entire joint area. In any case, the purpose is to obtain and maintain uniformity of metal temperature.

The filler metal is most commonly face fed in manual torch brazing operations. In mechanized operations, proper design will permit the use of pre-placed filler metal in the form of rings, washers, shims, paste or powder. However, the preplaced filler metal should be positioned with respect to the flame so as not to be prematurely melted.

Furnace Brazing

Furnace brazing is used extensively and furnace manufacturers build furnaces specifically for this method of metal joining. The process is not limited to any one base metal nor to any one brazing filler metal, but is governed by a combination of factors which will be mentioned in detail.

Equipment. The furnace for brazing may be electric, gas or oil fired, although for certain brazing operations one type is preferred over another. The type of furnace finally selected must be of suitable construction to provide the proper temperature, time and atmosphere. Accurately calibrated controls for both temperature and atmosphere suitable for the service intended, are required. In conveyor-type furnaces, the speed through the furnace must be controlled as this governs the time at temperature for a particular brazing operation.

Design of Joints. Joints should be specifically designed for furnace brazing. If possible, the brazing filler metal should be preplaced inside the joint adjacent to the heaviest member. This will prevent the light gage filler metal from melting and flowing before the parts to be brazed have reached the brazing temperature.

Since the entire assembly is raised to the brazing temperature, specific consideration must be given to metal expansion to obtain correct joint clearances at brazing temperature. This differs from localized heating methods where only the joint and immediately adjacent areas are heated. It is desirable to design the assemblies to be self-jigging. Any jigs used to align the parts for brazing will be heated to the brazing temperature and, therefore, for economy they should be kept small in size and in number. It is important that all components of a sub-assembly intended for furnace brazing be able to withstand the brazing temperature. In many instances it may be advisable to use heat shields around light gage sections to retard heating.

Filler Metals and Fluxes. Filler metal is preplaced in the form of shims, washers, rings, paste or powder. As mentioned in Chapter 4, certain fluxes have shorter life spans at brazing temperature than others, and this characteristic, together with the time of the brazing cycle, should be considered in the selection of a flux. Even when controlled atmospheres are used, it is sometimes advisable to include a small amount of flux in the joint area.

This flux addition counteracts the effects of oxidation which may take place before the assembly reaches the temperature at which the atmosphere is effective. Care must be taken in use of the flux to avoid undue damage to the furnace.

Brazing Procedure. The parts to be brazed must be properly cleaned. Flux, if necessary, is then applied and the parts assembled with the filler metal preplaced.

Before charging the furnace it should be brought up to temperature and properly purged (when a controlled atmosphere is used). See Chapter 4 for precautions to be taken in maintaining purity of atmosphere. See Chapter 23 for safety precautions to be taken. It is recommended that the furnace temperature be approximately 100 to 150 F above the liquidus of the filler metal.

Unless a thermocouple can be placed adjacent to the joint area, it is advisable to work out a suitable time schedule. Where the quantity of work is small and experimental work to establish a cycle is not warranted, the temperature can usually be approximated by observation through the door or other suitable port in the furnace.

Provision should be made for cooling the parts after brazing. When a controlled atmosphere is used during brazing, the parts should be cooled in the protective atmosphere. In all cases it is necessary to prevent relative motion between parts of the joint until the joint has gained sufficient strength upon cooling.

Induction Brazing

Careful consideration must be given to the equipment available, metals to be joined, joint design, induction coil design, filler metal temperatures, fluxing and jigging. Each of these factors is important in itself and in conjunction with the others. By balancing all of the factors properly, a wide range of base metals can be induction brazed.

Equipment. Induction brazing equipment is of three main types, namely motor generator, spark gap and vacuum tube units. For classification purposes, it can be said that motor generators are low frequency (up to 10,000 cycles), spark gap units are medium frequency (20,000 to 300,000 cycles), and vacuum tube oscillators are medium to high frequency (200,000 to 5,000,000 cycles). Manufacturers of this equipment produce standard power sources in various electrical capacities and couple these power units to work tables designed for general or specific applications. The selection of the proper capacity power unit is dependent on the part to be brazed and the production expected. Usual practice is to develop the information needed for capacity selection by experimental brazing on an induction heating machine.

An integral part of the induction heating equipment is the inductor coil (or block), called the *work coil*. Most work coils are of simple construction and can be fabricated by the user. The coils are constructed of copper usually in the form of tubing, but may be made of a block of copper which has been machined to allow for an internal water passage. It is essential that the work coil be cooled during the brazing cycle by means of circulating water. Small tube units of ¾ KW capacity may have the work coils air cooled.

The work coil must be tailored to heating requirements of the part for maximum efficiency. It is possible to use oversized, general-purpose coils for more than one joint design, within the limits of power available. The number of turns of copper tubing or the thickness of the copper block is dependent on the extent of the heat zone desired. Coil design must allow for *corner effect* in rectangular parts and surface irregularities which will be in the heat zone.

The gap between the work coil and the part to be brazed is known as *the couple*. By varying the couple from *close* (small gap) to *loose* (wide gap) over different portions of the same part, variations in the amount of heat input can be obtained. This is very important where a change of section brings both heavy and light masses into the joint area. Both sections can be brought to the brazing temperature uniformly by forming the work coil with the proper coupling for each section. Multiple work coils are available in which several units are brazed at one time.

It is possible to heat too rapidly by induction heating. Sufficient time for the filler metal to flow properly and form good fillets must be provided. It is usually better practice to use multiple work coils with the full capacity of the machine and heat over a reasonable time, such as 30 to 60 seconds, rather than to use a single work coil and attempt to braze in 5 to 10 seconds. The production rate in every case should be the same. Too rapid heating can also cause stress corrosion cracking. See Chapter 2.

Design of Joints. Since induction brazing involves localized heating, the design should take advantage of this factor. Subassemblies can be built up by step-brazing or by using two separate brazes, using the same filler metal, provided the heated zone does not extend to the previously brazed joint. It is also possible to braze assemblies which contain parts or areas that would be adversely affected by the brazing temperature.

Induction brazing is most efficient when jigging is limited to locating fixtures firmly affixed to the work table.

Very close attention must be given to the proper joint clearance with induction brazing because with this process, the heat may be induced in only one component of the joint causing it to heat faster and thereby expand more rapidly than the other. This could produce a very undesirable, uneven heat condition during the brazing cycle and should be compensated for in the initial joint clearance. For example, if the joint clearance increases during the brazing cycle, this should be compensated for by reducing the initial clearance of the cold parts and vice versa.

Filler Metals, Fluxes and Atmospheres. The filler metals are usually preplaced in the form of rings, washers or shims. There are some paste and powder applications but these forms do not lend themselves readily to the physical operations of induction brazing.

Where flux is required because of the filler metal and/or base metals employed, the primary consideration for selection is the brazing temperature of the filler metal. Induction brazing, involving a rapid heating method, minimizes the problem of time at temperature.

Induction brazing with an active or protective atmosphere is performed satisfactorily. Where a protective atmosphere is used, a small amount of flux must sometimes be inserted in the joint area to protect against oxidation until the atmosphere reaches its effective temperature.

Brazing Procedure. The parts should be properly cleaned, fluxed, if necessary, and assembled with the filler metal preplaced. This work may be done in advance but a note of caution is warranted. This type of brazing involves a considerable amount of handling, and there is a possibility of flaking-off the flux when it has dried.

Completely prepared parts are placed in the work coil in the locating fixture. This should automatically establish and uniformly maintain the amount of coupling between the coil and parts. Automatic timing devices are almost a necessity for economical operation. They permit the brazing operator to establish the time cycle and keep it uniform from piece to piece, within fractions of a second. Where it is desirable to force cool within the work coil, the timers can be preset to turn on a cooling medium, such as an air blast or water spray, and control its cycle. A water quench should only be used after the braze has cooled sufficiently to develop enough strength to hold the parts together.

Resistance Brazing

Design of Joints. Resistance brazing is most applicable to joints which have relatively small areas. It is difficult to get uniform current distribution, and therefore uniform heating, if the area to be brazed is large or discontinuous or is very much longer in one dimension. Joints to be resistance brazed should have their parts so disposed that pressure may be applied on them without causing distortion in the parts at brazing temperature. Wherever possible, the parts should be designed to be self-nesting to eliminate the need for dimensional features in the fixtures. Parts should also be free to move as the filler metal melts and flows.

Brazing Equipment. One common source of current for resistance brazing is a stepdown transformer whose secondary circuit can furnish sufficient low voltage current (2 to 25 volts). The current will range from about 50 amperes for small delicate jobs to many thousands of amperes for larger jobs. Commercial equipment is available for resistance brazing. Spot welding machines of all sizes may be altered slightly for use in resistance brazing. Less pressure and a longer time of current flow is necessary than normally used for spot welding.

Electrodes for resistance brazing are made of high resistance electrical conductors, such as carbon or graphite blocks, tungsten or molybdenum rods or inserts, or even steel in some instances. The heat for brazing is mainly generated in the electrodes and flows to the work by conduction. It is generally unsatisfactory to attempt to use the resistance of the work pieces alone as a source of heat. The current requirements are high as in spot welding. It is difficult to allow time for the filler metal to flow without overheating. The rate of solidification is extremely rapid since the parts are in contact with cold electrodes.

Carbon or graphite blocks, rods or pencils are most frequently used since brazing filler metals will not adhere to them as they will to metals. Various grades of carbon or graphite are available with ranges of resistance and hardness which permit adaption to various jobs. Carbon or graphite is easily worked to the desired shape, but these parts must be considered expendable since they waste away quite rapidly. A coating of flux on the outside of the carbons tends to lengthen their life.

The pressure employed by the spot welding machine, clamps, pliers, or other means must be sufficient to maintain good electrical contact and to hold the pieces firmly together as the filler metal melts. Too high a pressure may crack the carbons. The pressure must be maintained during the time of current flow and must be maintained after the current is shut off and until the joint solidifies sufficiently to permit moving the assembly.

The time of current flow will vary from about one second for small delicate work to several minutes for larger work. The time of current flow is usually controlled manually by the operator who determines when the part is brazed by the temperature and extent of alloy flow. Standard timers used on resistance welding machines may also be employed.

Filler Metals and Fluxes. Brazing filler metal in the form of shims, washers, rings or powder is used. In a few instances, face feeding is possible. For copper and copper alloys, the BCuP alloys are most satisfactory since they are self fluxing. BAg alloys may be used but a flux or atmosphere is necessary. The flux is usually applied as a very thin mixture just before the assembly is placed in the brazing fixture and when the flux is wet. Dry flux is a good insulator and will not permit sufficient current to flow. In some instances, powdered filler metal is mixed with a thin flux in a shallow pan to assure electrical contact and initiate current flow. One part is dipped in this pan to obtain both flux and filler metal prior to placing the part in the brazing fixture. Liquid fluxes, not ordinarily recommended for brazing, are suitable for resistance brazing in some instances.

It is possible to resistance braze without flux in a reducing atmosphere. The difficulty of maintaining the atmosphere is responsible for the rarity of this operation.

Aluminum alloys and magnesium alloys are seldom resistance brazed.

Brazing Procedure. The parts to be brazed must be clean. The parts, brazing filler metal and flux, if used, are assembled and placed in the fixture and pressure applied. As current flows, the electrodes become heated, frequently to incandescence, and the flux and filler metal melt and flow. The current should be adjusted to obtain uniform and rapid heating in the parts. If too much current is employed, the electrodes will get too hot and waste away rapidly. There is also danger of burning or melting the work. If too little current is employed, the time of brazing will be excessive. The current can be adjusted by varying the voltage of the transformer and/or using more of the electrodes or higher-resistance electrodes in the circuit. A little experimenting with electrode composition, geometry and voltage will give the best combination of rapid heating with reasonable electrode life. The pressure should never be interrupted during current flow or arcing will occur and the assembly will frequently be spoiled. The pressure must be maintained after the current is cut off to permit the brazing filler metal to solidify and gain enough strength before it is moved. Quenching the parts from an elevated temperature will help in obtaining the least amount of annealing and in flux removal. Such quenching should only be done after the assembly has cooled sufficiently to permit the braze to hold the parts together.

Dip Brazing

Two methods of brazing are employed; one, molten metal dip brazing and the other, molten chemical (flux) bath dip brazing.

Molten Metal Dip Brazing. This method is usually limited to brazing small assemblies, such as wire connections or metal strips. A crucible, usually made of graphite, is heated externally to the required temperature to maintain the brazing filler metal in fluid form. A *cover* of flux is maintained over the molten filler metal. The size of the molten bath (crucible) and the heating method must be such that the immersion of parts to be brazed will not lower the temperature of the bath below that necessary for brazing. Parts to be brazed must be clean and protected with flux prior to introduction into the bath.

Molten Chemical (Flux) Bath Dip Brazing. This method of brazing requires a suitable container, metal or ceramic, for the flux and a method of heating the flux to maintain it fluid. The heating methods used are externally as by torches; electrical resistance heaters within the bath; and heating the flux itself by the resistance loss (I^2R) of the molten flux. The third method requires melting the flux by external heating at the beginning of a run since the normally dry flux is not a conductor. The molten flux, however, does conduct electricity. Suitable controls are provided for maintaining the flux within the necessary brazing temperature range. The size of bath must be such that the introduction of parts for brazing will not lower the temperature below that necessary for brazing.

Parts must be cleaned and assembled and preferably held in jigs prior to immersion into the bath. Brazing filler metal is preplaced as rings, washers, slugs or as a cladding on the base metal. It is important that parts be dry since a violent explosion may occur when wet parts are immersed. A certain amount of flux adheres to the assembly after brazing, and this must be drained off while the parts are hot. Any flux remaining must subsequently be removed by washing in water or by a chemical means after cooling.

Block Brazing

This process, using heated blocks, requires proper heating of the blocks to obtain uniform and sufficient heat to obtain proper flowing of the filler metal. Filler metals are preplaced in the form of rings, washers, shims or paste. Proper fluxing must accompany the use of filler metal being used.

If there is much difference in cross section of the parts to be joined, preheating must be used to insure obtaining the proper heat for brazing.

The blocks act as a jig to hold the parts in alignment.

Flow Brazing

This process, using molten filler metal poured on the joint, must have all parts held in alignment by jigging. Preheating is advisable to shorten the brazing cycle and to minimize stress cracking, due to thermal shock.

Step Brazing

Step brazing is a technique which makes use of the differences of brazing temperature ranges of related types of brazing filler metals. By means of this technique, it is possible to braze one section of an assembly using the filler metal with the higher brazing temperature range. After brazing, any supplemental operations may be performed followed by another brazing operation using a filler metal with a lower brazing temperature range. The brazing filler metals are selected so that the temperature employed for the second braze does not seriously impair the braze made at the higher temperature. Step brazing involving three sequences has also been employed.

The brazing process used may be any of those mentioned but furnace, induction and resistance brazing have proven the most successful.

Brazing Vacuum Tubes

In addition to the procedures outlined in the preceding paragraphs, special processes have been developed in various industries to meet their specific requirements. This is particularly true in the electronic tube industry. Most electron tubes require a high vacuum for their satisfactory operation. If they are of the gas-filled variety, the purity of the gas must be maintained. High temperatures are encountered during processing and, in some cases, are maintained during service life. Cleanliness is of paramount importance in the preparation of all joints, and the metals must be degassed as much as physically possible. Vacuum brazing is often resorted to as it serves to maintain clean surfaces and permits outgassing at the same time that brazing is being performed. This process is actually a special form of furnace brazing.

Equipment. Vacuum furnaces for brazing may take a variety of forms and sizes. In general, a vacuum furnace is any enclosure suitably constructed to hold a vacuum and withstand the temperatures required for brazing. The source of heat is generally electric, as induction or resistance. (See induction and resistance brazing.)

Filler Metals and Fluxes. The brazing filler metals used in joining assemblies for vacuum tubes and similar devices must be selected with more than ordinary care. In order to maintain the required vacuum in the finished tube, materials which have a vapor pressure that exceeds the desired minimum pressure at operating temperatures cannot be used. This eliminates the use of any conventional fluxes and imposes much closer limits on the amount of impurities that can be tolerated in the filler metal. Brazing is done with filler metals, such as copper, silver, gold, platinum, nickel, rhodium and iridium and their alloys in an atmosphere of pure dry hydrogen or in a vacuum.

The filler metals are usually preplaced in a conventional manner in the form of rings, washers, shims or paste. For some applications, compounds of the filler metal are used which are decomposed or reduced during the brazing cycle. Copper oxide, silver oxide, silver nitrate, platinum chloride are thus applied in paste form or as a solution for brazing very small parts where there is not space available to preplace filler metal of the usual sizes.

Brazing Procedure. The brazing procedure used will be that used in the furnace brazing process. It must be remembered that extreme care must be taken in the cleaning of the parts and maintaining cleanliness prior to and during the brazing cycle.

Chapter 10

POSTBRAZE OPERATIONS

After the brazing operation it is always necessary to postclean if a flux is used and it may be necessary to heat treat the brazed parts depending on the brazing procedure and the service requirements of the parts.

Parts that have been brazed in a controlled-atmosphere furnace should be bright and clean if the proper procedure has been used. However, if the brazing operation is of a type that requires flux, it is necessary to remove the residue completely in order to insure against corrosion in service. Some flux residues are soluble in hot water and parts can be cleaned by immersion in fresh, running hot water. See Chapter 4, page 39. Parts that have been overheated during brazing may have some burned or blackened residue that will not be completely removed by hot water cleaning. In such cases, a subsequent dip in a chemical bath or sand or grit blasting may be necessary. Nitric acid is not recommended where brazing filler metals containing copper or silver are used. After a chemical dip, parts should be thoroughly washed free of any chemical and dried.

Parts which are to be subjected to reversals of stresses in service or which must be gas tight and which have been brazed with a silver alloy (BAg) filler metal should be slowly cooled to at least 800 F before quenching. Micro-cracking may occur in the brazing filler metal if the cooling rate is too rapid in the higher temperature ranges.

It is possible to combine heat treating operations with brazing operations by selecting a filler metal with a suitable brazing temperature range relative to the heat treating range of the base metal.

A filler metal may be selected with a higher solidus temperature than the heat treating temperature for post-brazing heat treatment or one having a lower solidus temperature for pre-brazing heat treatment. A third arrangement may be to select a heating cycle which will cause the filler metal to flow and accomplish heat treatment in the same operation.

Any particular operation will require special selection of filler metal and operating sequence to obtain proper results for the particular base metal, joint, and service conditions.

Chapter 11

INSPECTION

Inspection is the last of a series of basic steps in the control of brazing as a means of fabrication. Inspection procedures in every case may be simplified and the number of rejects reduced or eliminated by careful application of the design and production information given in preceding chapters together with an intelligent choice of brazing processes, brazing filler metal, joint design, cleaning methods, etc.

The methods of inspection to be employed are generally determined by the application for which an assembled part is to be used and in many cases inspection procedures are specified by the ultimate user or by a regulatory code.

Pre-production and workmanship samples are often used for comparison purposes during production. They may be sample specimens made during the development of the brazing procedure to be used or may be samples taken from actual production. In any case they show minimum acceptable production quality of the brazed joint. They are used to show the fillet sizes, amount and extent of allowable voids in a joint, etc., and serve as a ready reference for inspection.

Inspection tests fall into one of two classifications: nondestructive and destructive.

Nondestructive Tests

Visual examination is probably the most widely used of the nondestructive methods of inspection. However, as with all methods of inspection, visual examination will not be effective if the joint cannot be examined readily or if adhering flux interferes with such examination. Visual inspection is also a convenient preliminary test where other test methods are used.

When brazing filler metal is fed from one side of a joint or preplaced within the joint at or near one side of the joint in such a manner that visual examination of the opposite side of the joint after brazing shows a thin, even fillet of filler metal present, it can be logically assumed that a sound joint has been attained. If filler metal is applied from the same side of the joint that must be inspected it is possible, through improper practices, to get a good appearing fillet on this side of the joint without any penetration through the joint

Pressure testing is necessary where gas or liquid tightness is required of a joint. Joints subjected to low pressure may be tested with air but for reasons of safety, joints designed for high pressure service should be tested hydrostatically. Gases such as helium and "Freon" are also used. However, if a gas is used, it should be inert and not be harmful if a leak does occur. Test pressures are always greater than required service pressures and are usually specified by code or by purchase specifications.

Fluorescent and dye penetrant inspection is used for the detection of defects extending to the surface of both magnetic and nonmagnetic materials. It is used to a large extent in testing brazed joints in stainless steels, which may be subject to stress corrosion cracking.

The electrical resistance method of evaluating brazed joints depends on the variations in voltage drop across a constant cross section of metal. A relatively small current is passed from one contact through the work piece and brazed joint to a contact on the other side. The voltage drop across the work piece is then measured by means of a Kelvin Double Bridge. A void in the joint necessitates the current traveling a longer distance, thus showing up as an increase in voltage drop.

Radiography is used to some extent for examination of brazed joints. As a general rule, sections which are of uniform thickness and not too thick may be radiographed if an exposure can be made straight through the joint. Angular views, or those taken from the side of a joint, are misleading. Views which include two sides of a joint, such as one taken through a pipe fitting, must be interpreted with particular care.

Destructive Tests

Destructive methods of test are usually employed for selective or lot testing of brazed joints.

In lot testing, a small specified percentage of all production is tested to destruction. The results of these tests are assumed to apply to the entire production and all of the joints in the various lots or batches are accepted or rejected accordingly.

When used as a check on some nondestructive method of inspection, such as visual examination, a production joint may be selected at regular intervals and tested to destruction so that rigid control of brazing procedures is maintained.

The peel test is generally employed for shear or lap joints. One part is held rigid, as in a vise, while the other is peeled away from the joint. The peel test may be used as a means of production quality control to determine the general quality of the bond and the number of voids in the joint. For most applications, voids which are distributed homogeneously throughout may occupy as much as 25 per cent of the total area of a section. In the case of government applications, such as U.S.A.F., and for more critical work the voids must usually be held to a maximum of 15 per cent of the total area.

Tension or shear tests are usually used to determine the strength of a joint. Such tests are more often used in the laboratory to determine basic strengths of filler metals and the adequacy of proposed joint designs. These tests can be used for verifying the relative strengths of the joint and base metal parts. Tension and shear tests have been used to advantage in determining basic joint strengths for service below and above room temperature. These tests are used more widely for development than for production quality control, although they have been used for testing selected samples.

Fatigue tests are used to a limited extent and in most cases are a test of the base metal as well as the brazed joint. As a general rule, fatigue tests require a long time to complete and for this reason are very seldom used for quality control.

Impact tests like fatigue tests are generally limited to laboratory work in determining basic properties of brazed joints. As a general rule the normal notch-type specimens do not appear to be best for brazed joints. Special types of joints may be required to get accurate results at below and above room temperature.

Figure 11.1. Void (arrow) in tubular assembly

Torsion tests on brazed joints find quite a bit of use in production quality control. This is especially true where a stud, screw or tubular member is brazed to a heavier section.

For fuller details on any of the above test methods refer to the "Welding Handbook," Third Edition.

Typical Defects and Their Causes

When defects are found in brazed joints it is an indication that some part of the brazing procedure is out of control or that improper technique has been used. Several typical defects have been included in this chapter so

Figure 11.2(a). Section through brazed copper assembly

Figure 11.2(b). Photomacrograph of area in Fig. 11.2(a).—25X

that they may be recognized when they occur. The possible cause is given in each case.

Fig. 11.1 is a half-section of a copper capillary tube (center) brazed into a stainless steel assembly (shown in black). Note the pronounced void, caused by a gas pocket, in the fillet on the right side. This void was detected by subjecting the assembly to an air pressure and submerging it.

Figure 11.3(a). Failure to obtain flow of filler metal into joint

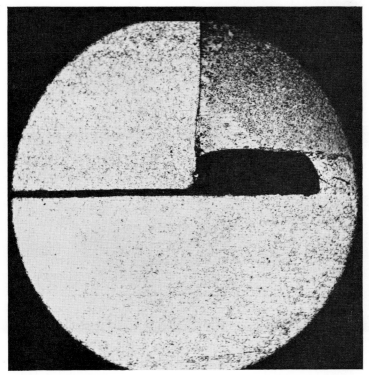

Figure 11.3(b). Photomacrograph of area in Fig. 11.3(a).—25×

Radiograph

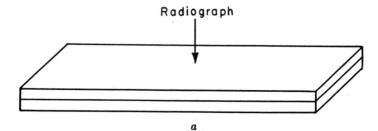

a

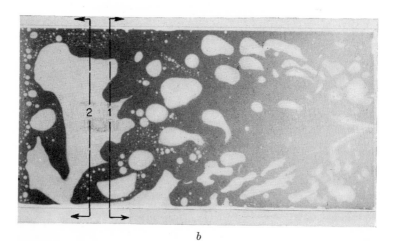

b

c

Figure 11.4. (a) Two flat pieces of steel brazed together; (b) Radiograph of assembly shown in Fig. 11.4(a); (c) Section through areas shown in Fig. 11.4(b).

The probable cause of the void is insufficient heating. This is borne out by the incomplete penetration of the filler metal into the joint.

Fig. 11.2(a) shows a section through a brazed copper assembly. Fig. 11.2(b) shows a 25✕ magnification of the section located by the arrow in Fig. 11.2(a). The voids and incomplete penetration of the filler metal through the joint are caused by insufficient heating. Such a defect being internal is detectable by a torsion or other mechanical test. It is sometimes revealed by a pressure test, if the joint contains voids which produce leakage.

Fig. 11.3(a) shows a joint without any flow of filler metal through the joint. The large fillet, located on the side from which brazing was done, is no indication of filler metal flow through the joint. A fillet on the other side would be evidence of full filler metal flow. Figure 11.3(b) shows a 25✕ magnification of the joint at the point located by the arrow in Fig. 11.3(a).

Fig. 11.4(a) shows a brazed joint which has been radiographed, Fig. 11.4(b), and sectioned, Fig. 11.4(c). The assembly shown in Fig. 11.4(a) is of two flat pieces of low carbon steel brazed with BAg filler metal. The radiograph was taken through the joint as shown. In Fig. 11.4(b) the white areas represent voids. The dotted lines show the locations of the sections in Fig. 11.4(c). Note the voids.

Chapter 12

ALUMINUM AND ALUMINUM ALLOYS

The practices for brazing aluminum alloys are similar to those used for ferrous metals except that the filler metals are aluminum-base alloys and the brazing temperatures consequently are closer to the solidus of the base metal.

Not all aluminum alloys can be brazed as it has not yet been possible to develop filler metals with a low enough brazing temperature. Filler metals recommended for brazing are listed in Chapter 3. It is possible to attain lower melting ranges by alloying aluminum with various combinations of zinc, copper, or other metals with or without silicon. While some of these combinations may have good characteristics from the standpoint of brazing procedure, none have been developed in which the resistance to corrosion of the brazed parts is not lowered. The degree of loss of corrosion resistance is difficult to express in specific terms, but the loss is sufficient so that such compositions are practical for only a few applications.

There are a number of heat treatable and nonheat treatable aluminum alloys that can be brazed. The heat treatable alloys suitable for brazing may be described generally as being of the magnesium-silicide type. These alloys have a brazing temperature range above that of the liquidus of the filler metal. Higher strength wrought aluminum alloys such as those containing copper or zinc as alloying constituents, are not suitable for general purpose brazing by the usual commercial practices as the melting temperature of these materials is lower than that of the filler metals shown in Chapter 3. The melting range and physical properties of typical wrought aluminum alloys that are brazable are shown in Table 12.1.

Standard brazing processes are used when brazing the aluminum alloys. These include torch, twin-carbon arc, furnace, induction, dip, and block brazing. Procedures for flow brazing and resistance brazing have not been developed but presumably these heating methods could be adapted to brazing the aluminum alloys.

In considering all of these brazing processes it is essential that adequate temperature control be maintained. This is accomplished in all but torch and twin-carbon arc brazing by providing automatic control that will hold the temperature within ±10 F of the nominal brazing temperature and provide a means to insure a temperature distribution throughout the brazing chamber that is within these same limits. In manual torch and twin-

TABLE 12.1. TYPICAL PHYSICAL PROPERTIES OF BRAZABLE ALUMINUM ALLOYS

ASTM No.	Aluminum Association No.	Commercial No.	Specific Gravity	Weight (Lb/Cu In.)	Approximate Melting Range (F)
990A	1100	2S	2.71	0.098	1190–1215
M1A	3003	3S	2.73	0.099	1190–1210
MG11A	3004	4S	2.72	0.098	1165–1205
GS11B	6053	53S	2.69	0.097	1075–1205
GS11A	6061	61S	2.70	0.098	1080–1205
GS10A	6063	63S	2.70	0.098	1140–1205
G1A	5050	50S	2.69	0.097	1160–1205
—	6951	J51S	2.70	0.098	1025–1200
—	6062	62S	2.70	0.098	1080–1205
ZG61B[1]	—	A612	2.81	0.102	1105–1195
ZG61B[2]	—	C612	2.84	0.103	1120–1190
ZG61A	—	40E	2.84	0.103	1120–1190

[1] Sand cast.
[2] Permanent mold cast.

carbon arc brazing the temperature is maintained by skillful judgment of the flux color and the melting and flow of the filler metal.

Conventional brazing procedures are used for brazing the aluminum alloys with the exception that in dip brazing the bath is composed of molten brazing flux instead of a salt or metal bath. The bath is used both to heat the part to the brazing temperature range and to remove the oxide coating.

A brazing flux is essential for aluminum brazing operations. All aluminum brazing fluxes are made in the form of powder. Brazing fluxes are applied dry or by mixing with tap water or alcohol for either painting, spraying or dipping. Dry flux is applied by either sprinkling on the work or by dipping a heated rod of filler metal in the flux. A mixture of two-thirds flux and one-third water by weight is usually satisfactory for painting. A thinner mixture is used for spraying or dipping and the amount of water needed is determined by trial to suit the parts or the spray gun used. Application of flux by spraying should be done in a conventional spray booth or with equipment that will insure the collection of spray waste. If standard paint spray guns are used, the lines and nozzle must be washed after use to prevent corrosion or clogging of the gun.

Care should be taken in handling aluminum brazing fluxes. See Chapter 23 for further information.

Filler Metal Forms

Filler metal for brazing the aluminum alloys is supplied in the form of wire or shims or in special sheets on which a uniform coating of filler metal is integrally bonded to the base metal.

Round wire of various sizes is used in the form of rings or in straight sections as required for preplacement. Shims are made from flattened wire or from sheet and the geometry is adapted to the shape of the parts to be brazed.

When the filler metal is applied as an integral coating to the sheet the product is designated *brazing sheet*. The coatings (BAlSi-2) are composed of aluminum-silicon alloys and may be applied to one or both sides of the sheet. The bonding of the coating is done in rolling the sheet, and the result is a product that can be formed by drawing, bending or other processes that do not remove the coating. The formed parts can be assembled, fluxed and brazed without placing additional filler metal in the joint.

Brazing sheet is frequently used as one member of an assembly with the mating piece made from the base metal without the coating. The filler metal on the sheet flows by capillary attraction and by gravity to fill the joint.

The principal of applying an integrally-bonded coating has been applied experimentally to tubing as well as sheet. However, the method has not been developed for such products as wire, rod, bar, extruded shapes, rolled shapes, forgings or castings.

Material Preparation

Precleaning practices vary widely depending on the condition of the metal surface, the thickness of the material, the alloys to be brazed and finally the liquid- or gas-tightness required in the finished joint. Either light oil or heavy forming lubricant will interfere with the flow of brazing metal. Solvent-type cleaning operations to remove these materials have been quite satisfactory. The light oil used to protect sheet products during shipment in most cases does not interfere with brazing. However, solvent cleaning is usually desirable, particularly where a large surface area is exposed during brazing since the oil fumes generated may be an explosion hazard.

In many applications cleaning with an etchant is not required. This is true particularly on brake-formed or press-formed parts. However, parts formed in spinning operations usually have a heavy oxide coating that has been broken up by the spinning tool and is so embedded in the surface as to prevent uniform wetting by the molten flux and filler metal. In this case the conventional caustic etch or nitric-hydrofluoric acid etch is desirable*.

---

* Etchant-type cleaning may be done with a caustic or acid type cleaner. Two cleaning procedures and cleaner compositions are shown below. There are many proprietary cleaning solutions that are equally satisfactory.

    Caustic Cleaner
       Degrease: CCl_4 , etc. or any equal proprietary cleaner.
       Dip: 5% NaOH—140 F—up to 60 seconds.
       Rinse: H_2O—cold.

The same is true when model parts are produced in small quantities by hand hammering or similar methods.

Etchant-type cleaning, or at least vapor-degreaser type solvent cleaning, is desirable when brazing thin metal. Brazing of fins to tubes or extended surfaces for heat exchanger applications usually involves brazing sheet in thicknesses from 0.006 to 0.012 inch. The amount of filler metal available on sheets of this thickness is not great and uniform joints are obtained only if the surface conditions are uniform. A light etch is the best method of cleaning such material although good solvent cleaning is frequently sufficient.

Cleaning of the filler metal by an etchant is usually desirable. Filler metal made from wire, or shims made from flattened wire will flow more uniformly if its oxide coating formed in fabricating the wire is removed by etching.

Joint Types

Lap joints rather than butt joints are generally used for brazing aluminum and aluminum alloys (see Fig. 12.1 and Chapter 6). However, in making any kind of joint, press or tight fits must be avoided in assembling the parts to facilitate filler metal flow and minimize flux entrapment. Clearances up to 0.010 in. are suitable for joints with laps of less than $\frac{1}{4}$ in. long. Clearances up to 0.025 in. are used for longer laps. The correct clearance for any given joint is best determined by trial.

The joint design should permit easy assembly of the parts prior to brazing. Closed assemblies should be designed to provide for escape of the gases during brazing. It is preferable to design the parts to be self-jigging, as by lock seaming, or to be held in alignment by rivets or projections that remain on the part after brazing (see Chapter 8—Assembly).

Fixtures and jigs made of material other than aluminum must be designed carefully so that the difference in thermal expansion does not force the parts out of line. Aluminum fixtures are satisfactory only if made from an alloy that will not melt at the brazing temperature and only if so shaped that there is no contact between the fixture and the molten brazing flux and filler metal.

Dip: 50% HNO_3—cold—10 seconds.
Rinse: H_2O—hot or cold.
Dry

Acid Cleaner
Degrease: CCl_4 , etc or any equal proprietary cleaner.
Dip: 10% HNO_3 , 0.25% HF—cold—up to 5 minutes.
Rinse: H_2O—hot or cold.
Dry.

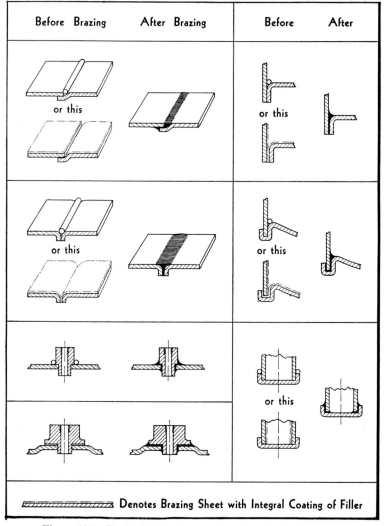

| Before Brazing | After Brazing | Before | After |

Denotes Brazing Sheet with Integral Coating of Filler

Figure 12.1. Typical joints for brazing the aluminum alloys

Performance of Joints

In all cases brazing temperatures exceed the temperature at which annealing occurs in the base material. It follows that furnace or flux bath brazed parts made from the nonheat treatable aluminum alloys have mechanical properties corresponding to the *O* or annealed temper of these materials.

The heat treatable base metals are also annealed by brazing but their strength can be substantially increased either by a heat treating operation applied after the parts are brazed or by quenching the part from the brazing temperature. The latter procedure is not always feasible and the results depend on the geometry of the part. The heat treatable base metals can be quenched in an air blast, a water spray or a tank of hot or cold water. A slight delay after removal from the brazing temperature is necessary to permit the filler metal to solidify before the part is quenched, otherwise, the dimensional changes that occur on quenching will open the joints. An air quench is the slowest quench of those mentioned above.

On some complicated parts cracking of the joints may occur even though the filler metal has solidified. In such cases the parts are allowed to cool and are heat treated in a separate operation. Since proper heat treating times and temperatures depend on the aluminum alloy involved, the manufacturer should be consulted for particulars.

No useful purpose is served by using a wrought heat treatable aluminum alloy for brazing unless the part is heat treated by one of the methods described above. The nonheat treatable materials are more economical in first cost and are equal in strength to the heat treatable alloys if the part brazed is not to be subsequently heat treated.

Resistance to corrosion of aluminum alloy base metals suitable for brazing is not lowered by brazing. Resistance to corrosion of brazed joints is of the same order as that of other welded joints. Parts exposed to atmospheric attack will not show a greater rate of corrosive attack at or near the brazed joints. Resistance to corrosion of the joints to specific chemicals cannot be described in general terms, but where other welded construction has been satisfactory brazed construction will usually be similar in performance. In other cases exposure tests under specific conditions are required.

In this connection, except where a noncorrosive flux is used, emphasis is again directed to the effect of incomplete removal of brazing flux. If the cleaning operations after brazing do not remove the flux, the combination of flux with moisture can result in solutions that will attack the metal. Such attack may not be enough to damage the part mechanically but it usually affects the appearance of the parts.

Furnace Brazing

Equipment for furnace brazing aluminum alloys is much the same as that used for heat treating these materials. Such equipment is designed to operate at temperatures up to 1200 F and may be heated electrically, or by oil or gas. Circulation of the furnace atmosphere to get a maximum rate of temperature rise improves the production rate of the furnace equipment and the flow of the flux and filler metal. A low rate of temperature rise on complicated parts such as radiators or heat exchangers results in a substantial lag in the temperature at the center of the part as compared to the outside. Therefore, circulation of the furnace atmosphere through the part is necessary to insure complete brazing at the center of the part.

The usual procedure is to adjust the furnace time from 30 seconds to 2 minutes longer than is required to bring the joint to brazing temperature. Too long a time at temperature may result in excessive diffusion, loss of control of filler metal flow, and attack from flux.

Experimental work in brazing aluminum alloys in the special nonoxidizing atmospheres used for ferrous materials has resulted in satisfactory brazing but not in improved flow or faster operation. Flux must still be used. The oxide coating on these materials is not changed appreciably by the brazing cycle. Consequently, an air atmosphere is quite satisfactory. Aluminum alloys are sometimes brazed to ferrous materials. In such cases a nonoxidizing atmosphere is used to protect the ferrous material.

Care to prevent contact of the molten brazing flux with metallic furnace parts is desirable because the flux will corrode any of the known furnace materials. This is usually done by providing shallow pans of ordinary steel to catch any flux that may drop. These pans can be replaced at a much lower cost than the furnace lining or the hearth parts.

In some cases brazing aluminum in furnaces that are used periodically for brazing steel with copper filler metal has resulted in rapid attack of the heating elements and furnace lining. This apparently was caused by the accelerated attack by the flux which occurs at the higher brazing temperatures used for the steel brazing operations after the furnace has been used for brazing aluminum.

Both continuous belt-type furnaces and batch furnaces have been used successfully. In some furnace designs, a fast rate of temperature rise is obtained by providing a high temperature zone at the entrance of the furnace in which the part is brought up to within 50 to 100 F of the brazing temperature and then moved to the brazing zone which is controlled to ± 10 F.

Dip Brazing

Dip brazing has been used widely particularly in the manufacture of heat exchanger assemblies. This process consists of dipping a part with preplaced brazing filler metal into a molten brazing flux. Thus fluxing and raising the part to brazing temperature are accomplished simultaneously. There are several pot designs and methods of heating the flux containers. The following are points to be considered:

Resistance heating of the bath is used almost entirely for production applications although externally-fired, gas-heated pots are adaptable to experimental and development work. Ceramic linings have been the only materials with sufficient resistance to provide a long life. Metal pots made from pure nickel have exhibited longer resistance than any other metal but not more than six months service can be expected. Intergranular corrosion of the pot occurs. Repair operations on cracked or leaky pots have not been successful because it is very difficult to determine where the corrosion ends when the corroded area is chipped out before the repair is welded.

Parts to be dip brazed are preheated prior to immersion in the molten brazing flux. Preheating temperatures range from 900 to 1050 F depending on the size and contour of the work. Preheating is applied to prevent solidification of the flux bath which occurs when a cold part is immersed and to dry the part eliminating possible rapid steam generation. Solidification of the flux insulates the part and closes small openings so that the molten flux cannot reach the inside.

Properly, flux must be dehydrated before use because chemically-combined moisture remains in the molten flux after melting. Dehydration is accomplished by immersing coils of aluminum sheet in the flux. As long as moisture is present hydrogen is evolved and ignited on the surface of the bath showing the characteristic small orange flames. Two or 3 hours of treatment are usually adequate to remove the moisture.

Torch Brazing

Torch brazing is accomplished manually by a process resembling gas welding. The essential difference is that the temperature of the parts is raised to a point where the flux is melted and the brazing filler metal is flowed into the joint without melting the base metal.

In torch brazing flux is mixed with water or used dry and applied to both the work and the filler metal by brushing, dipping or sprinkling. Oxy-acetylene, oxy-hydrogen, oxy-other fuel gas or air-fuel gas flames are used. The torch is adjusted so that the flame is on the reducing side.

Postbraze Cleaning

After brazing, corrosive flux should be removed. The flux is in the form of a hard, brittle layer and can best be removed by dissolution or chemical cleaning. Mechanical cleaning, such as wire brushing or grinding, is not adequate because it breaks up the crust of flux into fine particles that become embedded in the surface and on subsequent exposure to moisture may cause attack.

A number of methods are suitable for the removal of brazing flux. Immersion in hot water before the part has entirely cooled is effective in removing a major portion of the flux. For torch brazed joints particularly, the application of hot running water combined with brushing with a fibre brush is good practice. A 5-minute immersion in a 10 per cent nitric-0.25 per cent hydrofluoric acid bath or a 2- to 5-minute dip in a 1½ per

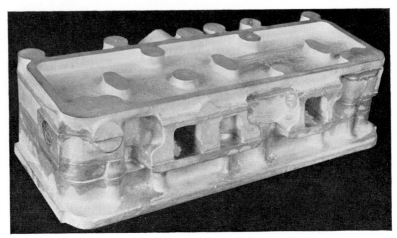

Figure 12.2. Cylinder head assembly made by brazing four castings

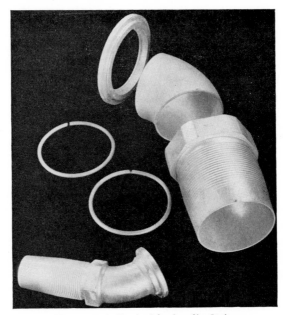

Figure 12.3. Brazed hydraulic fitting

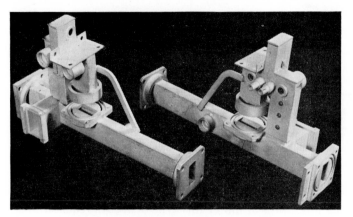

Figure 12.4. Dip brazed radar wave guide

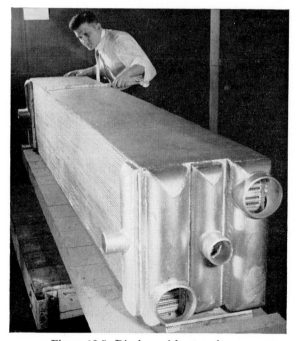

Figure 12.5. Dip brazed heat exchanger

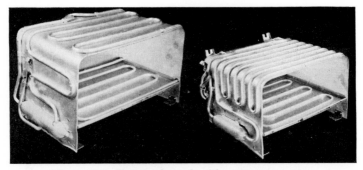

Figure 12.6. Furnace brazed refrigerator evaporators

cent hydrofluoric acid bath applied after a hot water dip will also remove the brazing flux. An acid dip of this type is always required if the joints are inaccessible for brushing. Equally good results can be obtained with any number of commercial cleaners. All these methods require a final clear water rinse to remove the cleaning agent.

Typical Applications

Fig. 12.2 shows a cylinder head assembly made by brazing four simple permanent mold cast sections. This is a good example of forming a complicated part by integrating a number of less complicated parts.

Fig. 12.3 shows a brazed hydraulic fitting made from a heat treatable aluminum alloy. Such fittings are used for pressures up to 2,000 psi.

Fig. 12.4 shows a dip brazed radar wave guide. This part contains sheet, tube, castings and forgings.

Fig. 12.5 shows a dip brazed heat exchanger made from aluminum alloy brazing sheet. This unit contains over 20 miles of brazed joints that must be pressure tight to 150 psi. The core is brazed and the headers are welded in position.

Fig. 12.6 shows furnace brazed aluminum alloy refrigerator evaporators made from tubing and sheet.

Chapter 13

MAGNESIUM

Materials

Because of the relatively high temperature required in the brazing process, only the M1A alloy can be brazed satisfactorily. The BMg filler metal, either of the commercial grade or one with a small amount of beryllium is used (see Chapter 23, Safety.). The beryllium is necessary only in furnace brazing to avoid possible ignition of the magnesium. Chloride-base fluxes (see Table 4.1, p. 35) are used to clean the metal and allow capillary flow to take place. Brazed joints offer good resistance against corrosion, but complete flux removal is of the utmost importance.

Design

Brazed joints should be designed to take advantage of capillary attraction and to allow the flux to be displaced by the brazing filler metal as it flows into the joint. Care should be used in the design of joints to minimize flux entrapment because of its corrosive nature. Lap and butt joints can be used for magnesium as with other metals. Clearances from 0.004 to 0.010 in. are satisfactory. It is best to design joints for the least clearance that will permit good flow of filler metal in order to take full advantage of capillary attraction. In chemical dip brazing the joints should have slots or recessed grooves for the filler metal to prevent its being washed into the flux bath. (See Figs. 6.6 and 6.8, pp. 57 and 58.)

Furnace and chemical dip brazed lap joints give tensile strengths in the range of 14,000 to 16,000 psi. Torch brazed joints, which were butt-brazed by allowing suitable clearance between the abutting edges for the filler metal to flow by capillary attraction, have given strengths of 18,000 to 23,000 psi.

Brazing Procedures

The factors involved in the brazing of magnesium are summarized in Table 13.1 for each of the three commonly used processes: furnace, torch, and chemical dip brazing. As with other metals, the parts should be thoroughly clean and free from all oil, dirt, grease and surface films such as chromates or oxides before brazing. The cleaning procedures are outlined in step 5, Table 13.1.

TABLE 13.1. BRAZING PROCEDURE FOR MAGNESIUM

	Brazing Process		
	Furnace	Torch	Chemical Dip
1. Brazing filler metal	BMg +0.002% Be (min.)	BMg	BMg
2. Alloy brazed	M1 sheet and extrusion	M1 sheet and extrusion	M1 sheet and extrusion
3. Brazing temperature range	1130–1160 F	1120–1160 F	1120–1130 F
4. Flux	Dry powder or chlorbenzol paste	Dry powder or alcohol	Both
5. Cleaning before brazing	*Mechanical*—Abrasion with steel wool or abrasive paper. *Chemical*—Degrease + 2 min. in bright pickle* solution.		
6. Equipment for heating	Electric or gas-fired furnaces. Control ±5 F	Oxy-acetylene or Air-natural gas	Electric or gas heated pots. Control ±5 F
7. Cleaning after brazing	Hot water +1–2 min. in chrome pickle* solution +2-hour boil in 5% sodium dichromate solution.		

* See Table 13.2.

The application of flux to the joints prior to brazing will depend on the brazing process used. Furnace brazing requires the use of dry powdered flux sprinkled around the joint. Water or alcohol pastes are unsatisfactory because the flow of the filler metal is reduced. Flux pastes made with benzol, toluene or chlorbenzol may be used but the applied paste is not smooth since the flux is not wetted by these liquids and is simply a suspension. These organic liquids are driven off by heating at 350 to 400 F for 5 to 15 minutes in drying ovens or circulating air furnaces. Flame drying should not be used as heavy soot will result. In torch brazing, water and alcohol flux pastes may be used but the alcohol paste is preferred due to better flow of filler metal.

For furnace brazing, electric or gas heating with automatic temperature controls capable of holding the furnace temperatures within ±5 F should be used. No special atmosphere is required but atmospheres such as those produced by the products of combustion of gas-fired furnaces or SO_2 reduce filler metal flow and should be excluded. Circulation of the furnace atmosphere is desirable since it reduces the heating time and results in more uniform heating. The brazing time will depend somewhat on the thickness of the materials used. Usually, one or two minutes at brazing temperature, exclusive of the time required to reach it, is sufficient but the time at temperature should be as short as possible to avoid diffusion. The brazed pieces are allowed to cool in air after removal from the furnace.

Torch brazing is accomplished using a neutral oxy-acetylene or oxy-other-fuel gas flame. An oxy-hydrogen flame may interfere with proper fluxing action if brought into direct contact with the flux. Heat is applied to the part until the flux melts and is continued with more care until a temperature is reached where the brazing filler metal melts and wets the surface of the base metal. The brazing filler metal should flow by capillary attraction. If the base metal is overheated, rapid diffusion and *drop through* of metal will result.

For chemical dip brazing, steel, nickel or clay-graphite crucibles are satisfactory containers for holding the molten flux bath. Parts should be preheated so that they are thoroughly dry before immersion in the bath. The flux is discolored in steel pots but the fluxing action is not affected. Either electricity or gas can be used for heating the pots. Because of the rapid heating of parts and the large volume of flux, better flow of filler metal is obtained. Also, lower temperatures, only a few degrees above the liquidus of the filler metal, may be employed. Temperatures of 1120 to 1130 F and times of 30 and 45 seconds are sufficient for a thickness of 0.064 inch.

After brazing, the joints should be washed in hot water within half an hour after they are cool enough to handle. The flux residues are quite hygroscopic and unless washed off will result in a pitting type of corrosion. The chrome-pickle treatment and the 2-hour boil in 5 per cent sodium dichromate can be applied anytime after the hot water wash. The compositions of the pickling solutions appear separately in Table 13.2.

Inspection

After cleaning, visual inspection may be used to reveal incomplete filler metal flow which could be attributed to insufficient cleanliness of parts,

TABLE 13.2. CHEMICAL TREATMENT SOLUTIONS

Treatment	Composition		Method of Application
Bright pickle treatment (before brazing)	Chromic acid	1.5 lb.	1 to 3 min. immersion followed by alkaline rinse, then cold and hot water rinses and air dry.
	Sodium nitrate	4 oz.	
	Calcium or Mg fluoride	⅛ oz.	
	Water to make	1 gal.	
	Temperature	70–90 F	
	Rinse solution:		
	Sodium Metasilicate	7 oz.	
	Water to make	1 gal.	
Chrome-pickle treatment (after brazing)	Sodium dichromate	1.5 lb.	1 to 2 min. immersion, hold in air 5 sec., followed by cold and hot water rinse, air or forced dry.
	Nitric acid	1.5 pt.	
	Water to make	1 gal.	
	Temperature	70–90 F	

Figure 13.1. Torch brazing hydraulic life floats

Figure 13.2. Longitudinal section of a completed float

insufficient flux or too low a temperature. The soundness of joints and bonding can be checked by cross-sectioning and examining visually under a microscope. Etching with 5 to 10 per cent acetic acid will reveal the bond zone. Flux inclusions and porosity can be detected radiographically on simple joints. For more complicated joints, exposure in a high humidity (95 per cent) atmosphere for 28 days will show any flux inclusions.

For further information on inspection see Chapter 11.

Typical Applications

Fig. 13.1 shows the torch brazing of magnesium hydraulic lift floats. BMg filler metal is melted into the annular groove and is distributed through the joint by capillary attraction. The flame is directed against the plug so that the tube walls are heated largely by conduction.

Fig. 13.2 shows the longitudinal section of a completed float.

Chapter 14

COPPER AND COPPER ALLOYS

Aside from the difficulties involved in the heating of high conductivity materials, brazing of the copper and copper-base alloys presents few problems if careful consideration is given to the brazing procedures used.

The large number of copper and copper-base alloys may be organized into groups with basically similar characteristics so that repetition may be avoided in presenting specific information regarding selection of brazing processes, filler metals, etc.

The copper alloys and copper itself are joined by all of the standard brazing processes (see Chapter 1).

Copper

Two types of copper are in general use today: oxygen-bearing copper and oxygen-free copper. The oxygen-bearing coppers comprise electrolytic (tough pitch) and fire-refined copper. The oxygen-free coppers include phosphorus-deoxidized and oxygen-free high-conductivity copper.

Electrolytic and Fire-Refined (Oxygen-Bearing Copper). These coppers are susceptible to oxide migration and/or hydrogen embrittlement at elevated temperatures. They contain from 0.02 to 0.05 per cent oxygen in the form of cuprous oxide which is generally distributed uniformly throughout the wrought copper

At high temperatures these oxides may migrate to the grain boundaries. Such concentrations, if not serious enough to adversely affect the tensile strength, will certainly reduce the ductility of the material so affected.

Hydrogen embrittlement occurs when the copper is subjected to an atmosphere containing hydrogen at elevated temperatures. As the rate of hydrogen diffusion into the copper is much higher than that at which the superheated water vapor can escape, the tremendous pressures built up result in the formation of voids in the copper. This phenomenon is also discussed in Chapter 2. On prolonged heating in such an atmosphere, the formation of these voids is cumulative and internal pressures are built up which are sufficient to cause rupture along grain boundaries.

In cases where oxide migration has already occurred and concentrations of oxide are present at the grain boundaries, hydrogen-created voids (embrittlement) are especially likely to occur. This results in serious impairment of all the mechanical properties of the base metal.

These functions, however, are controlled by factors of time and temperature. Rapid oxide migration does not take place until a temperature of 1680 F is attained. Hydrogen penetration of the copper takes place at temperatures above 750 F and increases sharply at temperatures above 1290 F.

Thus, in choosing electrolytic copper over an oxygen-free copper it is wise to consider the above factors where any brazing operation is to be performed.

Phosphorus-Deoxidized and Oxygen-Free Copper. The phosphorus-deoxidized and oxygen-free coppers do not contain copper oxide and are not subject to oxide migration or hydrogen embrittlement during brazing operations (see Chapter 2). For this reason they should be used whenever brazing is contemplated as a method of joining. These coppers may be brazed by any of the usual brazing processes employing any of the BCuZn, BCuP or BAg brazing filler metals with the exception of BCu.

The Brasses

The copper-zinc alloys are readily brazed by any of the standard processes. However, furnace brazing using a reducing atmosphere is not generally employed unless dissimilar metals are involved. The vaporization and oxidation of zinc in any but the driest atmosphere makes the use of a flux necessary even though a protective atmosphere is used.

Low brasses, those containing up to 20 per cent Zn, can be brazed with any of the brass (BCuZn) or lower brazing temperature filler metals (BCuP and BAg). However, due to the similarity of melting points between the high brasses (over 20 per cent Zn) and the brass (BCuZn) brazing filler metals, it is generally recommended that only the lower brazing temperature filler metals (BCuP and BAg) be used.

The common leaded brasses containing up to about 3 per cent lead can be brazed using BCuP and BAg filler metals if care is given to proper fluxing. If not, lead dross may seriously interfere with good wetting or proper flow of the brazing filler metals. The higher the lead content the more difficulty that can be expected in obtaining full strength joints.

The Phosphor Bronzes

The phosphor bronzes can be brazed by any of the standard brazing processes. The low tin varieties, Grades E and D, may be brazed using BCuP, BAg or BCuZn brazing filler metals. Those having higher tin contents, Grades A and C, have lower melting temperatures which makes it impossible to use BCuZn brazing filler metal. In the cold worked condition the phosphor bronzes are subject to "firecracking," (see Chapter 2), and rapid application of heat should be avoided.

The Silicon Bronzes

The copper-silicon alloys are readily brazed if adequate flux protection is supplied to prevent the formation of refractory silicon oxides. This metal must be in a stress-free condition during brazing in order to avoid stress cracking which may otherwise occur in the presence of molten filler metal (see Chapter 2). Stress relief may be accomplished by slow, careful application of the brazing heat.

This material is hot short and an assembly should be supported during the brazing cycle in a manner which will minimize any severe strain on the material (see Chapter 8). Filler metals of BCuP, BCuZn, and BAg classifications can be used.

The Aluminum Bronzes

The aluminum bronzes may be brazed if special care is taken to clean and flux the material properly. The joining of aluminum bronze to aluminum bronze or to other non-ferrous metals is readily accomplished with the use of suitable commercial aluminum bronze fluxes or one prepared by mixing one part of Type 1 flux to two parts Type 3 flux (see Chapter 4).

When joining aluminum bronze to ferrous materials the special commercial fluxes for aluminum bronze should be employed. A minimum heating time is necessary to avoid excessive diffusion of aluminum with the brazing filler metal resulting in the formation of a brittle joint interface. This condition is more pronounced with the higher aluminum content bronzes. Sometimes the use of brazing filler metals containing nickel gives improved results.

Copper-Nickel Alloys

The copper-nickel alloys may be readily brazed by any of the standard processes. This material must be in a stress-free condition during brazing in order to avoid stress cracking which may otherwise occur in the presence of molten filler metal (see Chapter 2). Stress relief may be supplied by slow, careful application of brazing heat.

Copper (BCu) filler metal may be used in brazing the cupro-nickels and is especially suitable in furnace brazing using the proper inert or reducing atmosphere. However, at brazing temperatures, copper brazing filler metal (BCu) may alloy excessively with the copper-nickel base materials as copper and nickel are soluble in each other in all proportions. This may result in the formation of an intermediate alloy having liquidus tempera-

Figure 14.1. Resistance brazing contact to brass part

Figure 14.2. Furnace brazed brass tubular assembly

tures with which it may be impossible to obtain complete joint penetration if too great a depth of joint is required. Conversely, such interalloying may in some cases extend into the base metal to such an extent that the base metal may collapse.

The nickel silvers (5 to 28 per cent Ni) may be brazed with any of the copper-zinc (BCuZn) or silver alloy (BAg) brazing filler metals but care

Figure 14.3. Torch brazing brass bar to copper ring segment

Figure 14.4. Resistance brazing braided copper to copper clips

Figure 14.5. 70-30 brass brazed with BAg filler metal

should be taken when the brasses are used because of their higher melting temperatures. Careless application of heat may result in melting the base metal.

Beryllium Copper

This alloy may be brazed with the silver alloy (BAg) filler metals if properly cleaned and fluxed. (see Chapter 23 for safety recommendations.)

Where heat treated material is to be brazed the use of a low temperature filler metal, such as BAg-1, and rapid localized heating is required to retain the best possible mechanical properties. Heat treatment of beryllium copper should be done subsequent to the brazing operation. If this is done, a brazing filler metal having a solidus higher than 1425 F is required as solution annealing of beryllium copper is accomplished at temperatures above 1425 F.

Figure 14.6. Brazing copper tubes to a cast iron header

Dissimilar Metals

Copper and copper-base alloys may be brazed to each other or to other ferrous and non-ferrous materials except aluminum and magnesium alloys if proper consideration is given to choice of filler metal, brazing process, etc.

In cases where materials have widely dissimilar coefficients of expansion, the design and execution of brazed joints having satisfactory characteristics may be extremely difficult or impractical.

Some of the copper-base alloys are subject to *firecracking*, which is caused by rapid heating of these alloys while containing residual stresses. Cold worked nickel silver, leaded brasses, leaded bronzes, and high tin bronzes are all susceptible to firecracking. Firecracking can be avoided by slow heating of stressed parts made of these materials or can be eliminated by a stress relief anneal at 500 to 600 F before brazing.

Typical Applications

Fig. 14.1 shows the resistance brazing of contacts to a brass member.

Fig. 14.2 shows a furnace brazed brass tubular assembly. The arrows show the locations of the brazed joints.

Fig. 14.3 shows the torch brazing of a brass bar to a copper ring segment using BAg filler metal.

Fig. 14.4 shows the resistance brazing of braided copper to copper clips for an electrical assembly.

Fig. 14.5 shows a thermo-switch assembly of 70-30 brass brazed with BAg filler metal.

Fig. 14.6 shows an example of brazing dissimilar metals. The components are a cast iron header and copper tubes.

Chapter 15

LOW-CARBON AND LOW-ALLOY STEELS

Low-carbon and low-alloy steels can be brazed successfully. The operation usually presents no great difficulty although the ease with which these metals can be joined is affected by their carbon content. The low-carbon steels are the easiest to braze.

For brazing carbon or low-alloy steels, copper-zinc brazing filler metals (for example BCuZn-3) are commonly used. When lower brazing temperatures are required silver-brazing filler metals such as BAg-1 to BAg-7 are employed.

The copper (BCu) and copper-zinc (BCuZn) brazing filler metals achieve high strength in shear and tension. They can be used in square butt joints, lap joints and T-joints. When the fit-up is irregular, BCuZn-3, -6, and -7 are more suitable. The last two classifications give good color match, but their brazing temperature ranges are higher.

The binary copper-phosphorus or the ternary copper-silver-phosphorus brazing filler metals (BCuP-1 to BCuP-5) are not recommended for brazing steel because of phosphorus embrittlement (see Chapter 2).

Brazed steel assemblies in carbon and low-alloy steels possess good mechanical properties. To achieve optimum results when brazing plain carbon or low-alloy steel, a suitable flux or atmosphere is necessary to protect the bonding surfaces and to promote good wetting.

On steel, brazed joints are usually designed to provide very close clearances betwen the members to be joined so that the brazing filler metal will flow through these clearances and fill them completely by capillary attraction. For this reason lap-type joints, which are generally subjected to shear stress, are designed with clearances on the order of 0.002 to 0.005 in. with all filler metals except BCu for which clearances of 0.000 (light press fit) to 0.002 in. are used. Experience has shown that the strongest joints are obtained with the smaller clearances. Such joints can also withstand the effects of severe shock and vibrations.

Brazing Procedures

Prior to brazing, it is imperative that the surfaces to be joined are clean and free of any dirt, scale, grease or oxides. Traces of oil and dirt left in the

108

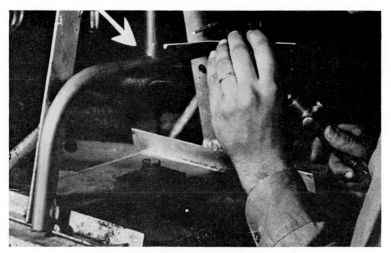

Figure 15.1. Torch brazing steel tubing

Figure 15.2. Preparation for furnace brazing

joint area will hinder the brazing operation and may cause excessive porosity and discontinuities in the joint.

All the common brazing processes are used to braze steel. Of these processes, torch, furnace and induction brazing are used most widely. The other processes find applications in specific instances for which they are already available or better adapted.

For manual torch brazing, the filler metal is usually face-fed into the pre-fluxed joint. In order to keep warping, distortion and metallurgical changes in the steel to a minimum, the base metal should not be overheated.

Where a large number of joints are to be brazed, it is desirable to preplace the filler metal. Furnace brazing in a suitable controlled atmosphere, using BCu filler metal, is good for brazing steel assemblies where mass production is involved and higher brazing heats are not objectionable.

Induction brazing is particularly applicable on parts which cannot or should not be heated in their entirety. BAg and BCuZn filler metals are used with their corresponding fluxes or atmospheres in these cases.

In brazing low-alloy steels it may be desirable to use a brazing filler metal which can be applied at temperatures lower than those which may cause hardening, i.e., which would not exceed the critical temperatures of the steel. Where the assembly is to be heat treated after brazing, the filler metal should have a solidus well above the heat treating temperature to avoid impairment of the joint.

When the brazing temperatures exceed the critical points of the steel, the brazing difficulties generally increase in proportion to the degree of hardening developed in the heat-affected zone. Since this hardening depends also upon the cooling rate from the brazing temperature, slow cooling rates which minimize hardening are beneficial. When rapid quenching is employed, cracking may occur due to differential temperatures or expansion rates.

Mild or low-alloy steel in the work hardened condition will experience a certain amount of softening in the heat-affected zone. This softening is minimized when a lower melting filler metal is used and when the time at temperature is kept as short as possible.

Typical Applications

Fig. 15.1 shows the joining of steel tubing by brazing. This has applications in metal furniture, aircraft, and other industries.

Fig. 15.2 shows the preparation for furnace brazing of steel flanges on to small steel tubes.

Chapter 16
STAINLESS STEELS

The brazing of stainless steel is neither a difficult nor an unusual operation in present-day manufacturing. However, proper brazing technique, materials and equipment are more important than for the brazing of most common metals.

This chapter deals with the brazing of stainless steels containing 16 to 26 per cent chromium and 8 to 25 per cent nickel, and chromium irons containing 11 per cent or more chromium. The steps involved in brazing these materials are the same as for carbon steel. However, some of the properties of these alloys introduce special problems which must be recognized and dealt with. See Chapter 2.

Stainless steels are used where resistance to one or more of a wide variety of corrosive media is required or where retention of strength and resistance to oxidation at high temperatures are necessary. Because of the range of operating conditions under which these steels are used, it is difficult, if not impossible, to predict the service life of brazed joints under specific conditions. It is, therefore, best to determine the suitability of the procedure and brazing filler metal by means of tests of joints under the contemplated conditions. However, where testing is impossible or not feasible the information in this chapter will provide the basis for a good approach to any problem. Of particular importance are the paragraphs under *Resistance of Brazed Joints to Heat and Corrosion*.

Base Metals

Chromium-Nickel Types. These steels generally are well adapted to joining by brazing. The unstabilized types such as 302, 303 and 304 are subject to precipitation of carbides along the grain boundaries when heated in the range of 900 to 1300 F. This precipitation impairs the corrosion resistance of these steels. The extent of carbide precipitation depends on time and temperature. Therefore, this effect can be minimized by making the brazing cycle as short as possible. With short-time brazing cycles these materials can be brazed without serious loss of corrosion resistance.

Carbide precipitation in stainless steels is virtually prevented by suitable additions of carbide stabilizers such as columbium or titanium to these alloys. Types 321 and 347 are so-called *stabilized stainless steels* and may

111

be brazed with many more brazing filler metals and longer brazing cycles with less danger of impairing corrosion resistance. Several of the unstabilized types are available with modified analyses such as Type 304L (ELC) in which the carbon content is less than 0.03 per cent. These low-carbon stainless steels can be joined by brazing with essentially the same range of filler metals and heating cycles as the stabilized types.

Precipitated carbides in stainless steels can be re-dissolved by heat treatment following the brazing operation if high-temperature brazing filler metals are used. For a more complete discussion of carbide precipitation see Chapter 2, page 15.

The chromium-nickel steels are subject to stress corrosion cracking in the presence of molten brazing filler metal. This phenomenon occurs when the base metal is under stress, either residual or resulting from applied loads while the braze is being made. The filler metal penetrates the base metal along the grain boundaries at the points of stress producing a greatly weakened base metal. Brazing should, therefore, be done on annealed temper material only. Parts must be assembled and supported in a manner so as to avoid stress during the brazing cycle. For a further discussion of this subject see Chapter 2.

Chromium Types. These steels have their own characteristics and in some instances can be substituted for the chromium-nickel types. Types such as 405, 410, 416, 420 and 440 are hardenable when cooled from temperatures higher than 1400 F. The lower temperature brazing filler metals should be used to avoid hardening of these alloys after brazing. These types are also subject to stress corrosion cracking (see Chapter 2). Type 430 is particularly subject to a kind of crevice corrosion which is discussed in this chapter on page 115.

Dissimilar Metals. All the stainless steels may be joined to other commonly used metals and alloys except aluminum and magnesium. When dissimilar materials are to be brazed, a flux must be selected which will be effective on both sides of the joint. This is also true if atmospheres are used. The filler metal must be compatible with the base metals on both sides of the joint.

Joint clearance, when the assembly is at room temperature, should be such as to obtain the correct clearance at brazing temperature. The coefficients of expansion of various metals are given in Appendix A. As in all brazing, the parts must reach the brazing temperature at or about the same time. Heat conductivity and the mass of the parts must be taken into account to obtain this result. As the dimensions at the joint become larger, it becomes more and more difficult to obtain a satisfactory joint, particularly if the coefficients of expansion do not match.

Filler Metals

Classifications BAg-1 through 7, BCu and BCuZn-1, 2, 3, 6 and 7 are usable as brazing filler metals for the stainless steels. Service conditions and the base metal will determine which type will be most satisfactory. Where corrosion is a factor, BAg-3 and BAg-4 filler metals are recommended over those classifications which do not contain nickel. BNiCr, BCu and BAgMn filler metals provide the highest strength at elevated temperatures of any of the filler metals available for brazing stainless steels (see Chapter 6). BCu, BNiCr and BAgMn filler metals are generally used for furnace brazing with high purity reducing atmospheres of extremely low moisture contents.

BAg-1 is a general purpose filler metal with good brazing characteristics. Its relatively low brazing temperature range makes it suitable for use on the unstabilized types of stainless steel. BAg-2 is also a general purpose brazing filler metal but requires a somewhat higher brazing temperature range. It is particularly useful where tolerances cannot be as closely controlled as is necessary for BAg-1. BAg-2 filler metal should not be used where the heating time is excessive due to its tendency to liquate. BAg-7 is important in stainless steel fabrication because of its white color and lack of cadmium which allows its use in fabricating food-handling equipment. BCuP filler metals are not satisfactory for brazing stainless steels. See Chapter 2 for information on phosphorus embrittlement.

Fluxes and Atmospheres

Chapter 4 should be consulted to obtain information on which to base a selection of fluxes or atmospheres. In the case of stainless steels, chromium oxides must be removed and prevented from forming. Special fluxes for this class of materials are required.

Fluxes should be applied in paste form so as to cover the joint area completely. Sometimes a relative motion between the parts serves to distribute the flux and thoroughly wet all surfaces.

Atmospheres for furnace brazing must be so constituted as to prevent the formation of chromium oxide. This requires atmospheres of high purity and adequate dryness.

Brazing Procedures

Any brazing process can be used to make brazed joints in stainless steel. Heating equipment must be designed and operated so as to secure the proper rates of heating. The unstabilized types of stainless steels should be heated and cooled quickly to minimize carbon precipitation. Heating in general should be rapid so as to prevent flux exhaustion before the brazing temperature is reached. The heating rate cannot be so high as to overheat the surface of the steel before the deeper parts of the joint are brought up to temperature. Differences in the mass of parts and dissimilar metals, if used, must be considered. The most commonly used brazing processes are torch, induction, resistance and furnace brazing.

Precleaning. Adequate cleaning of the joint area before brazing is very important. The need for perfectly clean joint areas is even more important for stainless steels than for carbon steels. In the case of carbon steels, fluxes can be depended upon to dissolve at least thin layers of oxide coatings but not so in the case of stainless steels. Adequate fluxing will, in general, only prevent the occurrence of oxides during the brazing operation. The corrosion resistance of stainless steel is due to an oxide coating which forms on contact with air. This oxide layer is highly refractory and its removal by mechanical cleaning just prior to the brazing operation is strongly recommended.

Mechanical cleaning can be done by using abrasive paper or cloth, filing or machining. Contaminants such as grease or oil must be removed prior to brazing. Production brazing preparations should consist of mechanical cleaning and degreasing just before assembly of the parts. When brazing an occasional joint, none of these steps should be omitted if a high quality joint is required. When proper precleaning is done, good brazed joints can be obtained when using the free machining types of stainless steels.

Postcleaning. The various standard methods of flux removal can be used on brazed assemblies of stainless steel such as cold or hot water rinse, proper chemical cleaning and mechanical cleaning combined with the foregoing. Nitric acid and hydrochloric acid as cleaning agents should be avoided where they are likely to affect the base or filler metal. Sometimes some stainless steels become oxidized in the heated area. If this oxide coating is thick, sand or nonmetallic grit blasting may have to be used. Steel shot is to be avoided as the steel particles may adhere to the stainless steel and cause rusting or become focal points for corrosion.

Resistance of Brazed Joints to Heat and Corrosion

A stainless steel is selected for a given application either for its resistance to heat or corrosion. The question can be logically asked, "Why use a stainless steel if it must be brazed with a material not as resistant to heat and corrosion?" The answer lies in the wide variety of brazing filler metals available which can be used on stainless steel. The silver alloy filler metals are resistant to many corrosive media which do not affect stainless steel. The joint area usually is small and deep compared to its frontal area and, therefore, presents only a small area for attack. For heat resistance there are available several standard and special filler metals very resistant to high temperatures.

Figure 16.1. Brazed stainless steel stop gear and cam

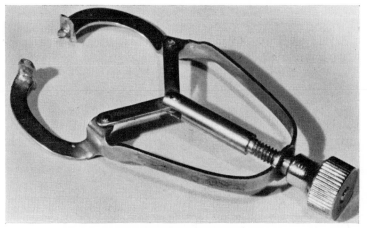

Figure 16.2. Brazed stainless steel dental appliance

Figure 16.3. Torch brazed stainless steel fastener

However, there have been some baffling failures of brazed joints in stainless steel made with BAg filler metals when the fluid in contact with the joint was apparently innocuous tap water. Early failure of joints in contact with water containing chlorine compounds have been observed.

Investigation has shown these failures were due to a breakdown of the bond between the filler metal and the stainless steel. This breakdown of the bond is believed to be due to an electrochemical action between the silver alloy filler metal and the stainless steel. This phenomenon can occur when the water in contact with the joint is still. Moving water tends to prevent the electrochemical process and the corrosive action is stopped. This type of joint failure has been called *crevice corrosion*.

Some investigators have shown that the addition of small percentages of nickel to the silver alloy filler metal will completely prevent the occurrence of crevice corrosion except in the case of 430 steel. Even with this steel the corrosion rate is slowed down to a remarkable degree. A special alloy containing tin and nickel is claimed to eliminate crevice corrosion completely in Type 430 steel. Many joints have been made with the various silver alloy filler metals in stainless steels with no service failures. However, careful consideration should be given to the fluids which will be in contact with the joints and the selection of the proper brazing filler metal.

Typical Applications

Fig. 16.1 shows a stainless steel stop gear and cam for a radio device assembled by brazing.

Fig. 16.2 shows a dental appliance of stainless steel in which the component parts were assembled by brazing.

Fig. 16.3 shows a stainless steel fastener which was torch brazed with BAg-4 filler metal.

Chapter 17

HIGH-CARBON AND HIGH-SPEED TOOL STEELS

By definition and usage low-carbon steels are those which contain a maximum of 0.30 per cent carbon; medium-carbon steels are those which contain from 0.30 to 0.45 per cent carbon; and high-carbon steels are those which contain more than 0.45 per cent carbon. Refer to Chapter 15 for information on the brazing of low-carbon and low-alloy steels.

Tool steels containing 0.60 to 1.25 per cent carbon are known as *carbon tool* steels. These steels must, except for thin sections, be drastically quenched to achieve maximum hardening in heat treating. Tool steels containing varying percentages of alloying elements to achieve special properties, such as less movement on heat treatment, greater wear resistance, more toughness or better high temperature properties, are referred to as *alloy tool steels*. No attempt will be made to classify these alloy steels. They are known by various trade names and grades and their properties and metallographic characteristics are adequately covered in the manufacturers' published information and in various handbooks.

High-speed steels although by definition logically falling into the alloy tool steel group are specifically mentioned because of their wide use in industry as metal cutting tools. The high-speed steels contain tungsten and/or molybdenum, chromium and vanadium as their principal alloying elements. A common analysis is known as 18:4:1—18 per cent tungsten, 4 per cent chromium and 1 per cent vanadium, respectively.

While sintered carbides do not fall under the classification of steels, their usage places them in the tool category. Since carbides are relatively expensive and inclined to be brittle when subjected to shock loads, general practice is to use relatively small tips of carbide which are brazed or otherwise fastened to a shank of steel. See Chapter 22 for further details.

These materials must be clean; that is free from oil, oxide, and other foreign material to secure satisfactory brazed joints. A machined or roughened surface is always preferable to a finish ground surface, since it is more difficult for the flux and brazing filler metal to wet and flow on a highly polished surface.

Joint clearances must be determined for each application taking into

117

account the expansion coefficient of the materials and the method of heating. A safe rule is to have joint clearances for BAg filler metals of 0.002 to 0.005 in. with greater clearances for the more sluggish filler metals. For copper brazing filler metal (BCu) a press fit is preferable.

The filler metal may be hand fed into the joint or preplaced. (See Chapters 3 and 6.) Flux is generally used except in those cases where an adequate reducing atmosphere is provided to prevent oxide formation. Brazing with copper filler metal is usually done in a controlled atmosphere. If a controlled atmosphere is used, decarburization should be guarded against.

As a rule brazing of high-carbon tool steels is best done prior to or at the same time as the hardening operation. The hardening temperature for carbon steels ranges from 1400 to 1500 F. Brazing filler metals having brazing temperature ranges above 1500 F are used for applications when brazing if done before heat treatment, and filler metals having a solidus near or below this temperature are used when brazing and hardening are done simultaneously. If the joint is in a noncritical area the part may be brazed after heat treatment providing the joint area can be heated locally without heating the rest of the assembly above its tempering temperature. Should critical portions be heated above the original tempering temperature, the hardness of the part may be lowered.

The successful brazing of alloy tool steels is dependent upon the knowledge of the particular steels involved. Alloy tool steels can have wide ranges of analyses, and therefore, wide differences of behavior on heat treatment and heating for brazing. Suffice it to say that the alloy steel in question should be studied carefully to determine its proper heat treating cycle, the kind of quench necessary (water, oil or air), the best brazing filler metal and the proper technique for combining the heat treating and the brazing operation so as to achieve the maximum properties in service life.

For the brazing of high-speed tool steels and some high carbon, high chrome alloy tool steels that have relatively high tempering temperatures, special brazing techniques may be used. These alloys are usually tempered in the range of 1000 to 1200 F. There are brazing filler metals that have brazing temperature ranges of 1100 to 1200F (see Chapter 3) thus making it possible to combine the tempering and brazing operations. The part may be removed from the tempering furnace, the braze made by locally heating the joint area and the assembly put back in the furnace to again equalize the temperature. This can be done with these materials with relatively low loss in hardness.

Brazing is very important in tool repairing. In this category each plant builds a "know-how" of repair knowledge which cannot be readily applied in another plant nor can it be explained in as short a discussion as this so as to be of material benefit to the user. The type of steel used, the nature of

Figure 17.1. Furnace brazed alloy tool steel

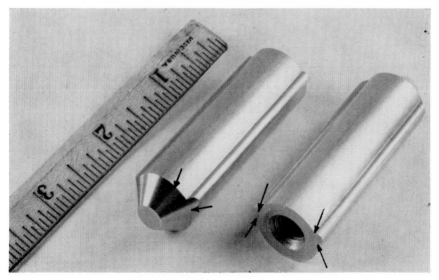

Figure 17.2. Alloy tool steel assembly

Figure 17.3. Photomicrograph of joint in fig. 17.2

Figure 17.4. Torch brazing high alloy tool steel

the tools, the facilities for brazing, and the development of a suitable brazing technique, are probably the most important factors. What has been stated concerning tool steels in general is applicable to the repair of tool steels by brazing. A few helpful general remarks follow. Tools which are to be repaired should be preheated in a furnace to as high a temperature as can be used without undue loss of hardness, the braze made and the parts returned to the furnace to avoid any sharp temperature gradients which may set up stresses sufficient to cause cracking in the base metal and consequent failure of the tool or brazed joint.

This information must be brief since each job will require a knowledge of the service requirements as well as the mechanical and metallurgical characteristics of the particular application. Specific details of various applications would tend to obscure the basic considerations rather than serve as a guide for other applications.

Typical Applications

Fig. 17.1 shows a furnace brazed assembly of 1.5 per cent carbon, 12 per cent chromium tool steel. The joint is at the juncture of the vertical and horizontal components. A copper brazing filler metal was used in a hydrogen atmosphere.

Fig. 17.2 shows a furnace brazed assembly of 1 per cent carbon, 5 per cent chromium and 1 per cent molybdenum tool steel. A BAg filler metal was used in a hydrogen atmosphere. Hardening was accomplished in conjunction with the brazing operation. Fig. 17.3 shows a photomicrograph of the brazed joint shown in Fig. 17.2.

Fig. 17.4 shows the torch brazing of a high alloy tool steel assembly.

Chapter 18

CAST IRON

There are several kinds of cast irons including white, gray, malleable and ductile. Typical compositions of cast iron are given in Appendix A. There are many applications in which it is desirable to braze gray, malleable and ductile irons either to themselves or to dissimilar metals. The white irons are seldom brazed.

It is only in the last few years that the brazing of ordinary gray cast irons using silver alloy filler metal has become commercially practical; the development of a satisfactory surface pretreatment has opened up many design possibilities. Intricate forms can be built up from simple castings or by joining castings to standard wrought forms such as tubing, rolled shapes, etc. Foundry work may be simplified by making intricate castings in several parts in order to reduce coring. Gray, ductile and malleable irons can be joined to most of the commercially important metals and alloys. The most common wrought metals used with these castings are ferrous base products.

In the brazing of ductile and malleable irons certain precautions are imperative and these are the same for either type. If ductile or malleable irons are heated above 1400 F the metallurgical structure may be damaged and brazing should be done below this temperature. Fig. 18.1 shows the relationship of time at temperature to the changes in malleable iron. Ductile iron behaves in a similar manner.

Metallurgical Considerations

When a gray, malleable or ductile cast iron is heated above its critical (transformation) temperature, the structure normally present begins to transform into austenite. Upon cooling, this new structure is converted either to martensite if the cooling rate is high, or to a fine pearlite structure having a cementite network. In either case, the metallurgical structure becomes extremely unfavorable in the heat-affected areas. The critical temperature varies with the composition and rises gradually with increased amounts of silicon.

Wetting

Graphitic carbon present in cast irons will not be wet by brazing filler metals and may prevent a good metallic bond. This creates a difficulty with gray irons. Little difficulty is encountered from this source with malleable and ductile irons.

Where wetting difficulties are encountered there are several cleaning methods available which can be used. One such method is a proprietary electrochemical surface cleaning method which produces a surface essentially free of graphite, sand, silicon, oxides, etc. The process employs a catalyzed molten salt bath operating at 850 to 950 F. Direct current is passed through the bath using the work as one electrode and the steel tank as the other. The direction of flow is occasionally reversed to produce reducing, oxidizing, and again reducing effects. A water rinse completes the surface treatment.

Other methods of cleaning include searing with an oxidizing flame, grit blasting and chemical cleaning.

Precleaning and Surface Preparation

It is usually desirable to machine or file the surface of a casting in order to secure uniform joint clearance. The casting "skin", which contains sand inclusions, is difficult to braze to without proper cleaning. The surfaces to be brazed should be free from dirt, oil, grease, etc. (See Chapter 7, Precleaning and Surface Preparation.) If necessary, the exposed graphite is removed following surface cleaning by the electrochemical method or one of the other methods mentioned above.

Filler Metals and Fluxes

With proper surface preparation, any filler metal suitable for use with iron or steel can be used for the cast irons. Those preferred, however, are the lower melting BAg filler metals. Those containing nickel, such as BAg-3 and BAg-4, have greater affinity for cast irons and therefore produce higher strength joints. Copper and copper-zinc filler metal can be used but great care must be exercised because of their higher brazing temperature ranges. Filler metals containing phosphorus (BCuP) are not suitable for joining cast iron due to the formation of brittle iron-phosphide constituents. Such joints, if made, would be extremely brittle. The AWS Brazing Flux Type No. 3 is employed with the recommended BAg filler metals.

Brazing Processes

Any of the brazing processes described in Chapter 1 are applicable to the brazing of cast irons. The choice of brazing process will depend upon the metals being joined, the brazing filler metals used, design of the joint and the relative masses of the parts. Those processes which lend themselves to automatic temperature control are desirable; overheating should be avoided.

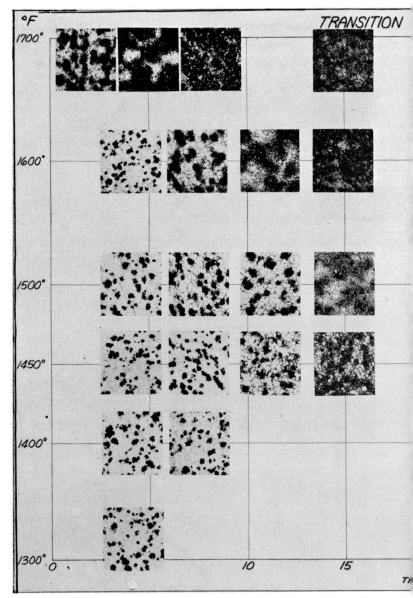

Figure 18.1. Relationship of time at te:

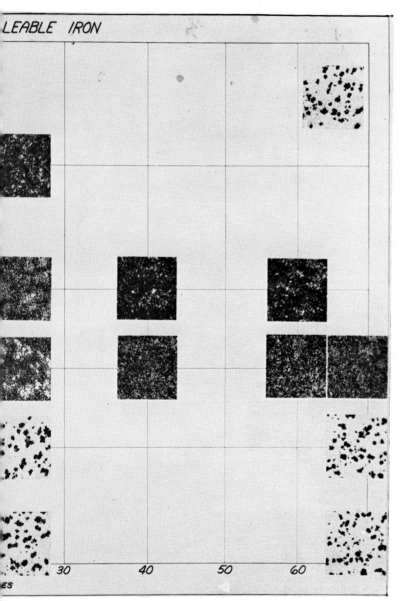

LEABLE IRON

30   40   50   60

ES

to the changes in malleable iron

Figure 18.2. Steel sprocket brazed to cast iron hub

Figure 18.3. Steel tubes brazed to malleable iron header

Joint Design

The general factors associated with joint design have been covered in Chapter 6.

Joint clearances should be determined for specific applications, considering the thermal expansion coefficients of the metals being joined, the methods of heating, type of filler metal, etc. The recommended joint clearance for optimum results is 0.002 to 0.005 in., with a maximum spacing of

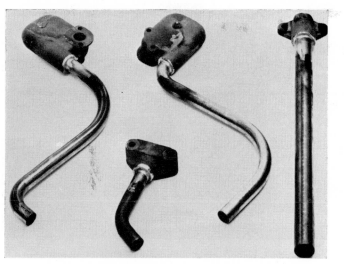

Figure 18.4. Cast iron fittings brazed to steel tubing

Figure 18.5. Steel tubing brazed to cast iron base

Figure 18.6. Brazing malleable iron elbow to pipe

0.01 inch. The variation of shear strength with joint clearance follows the same general pattern shown in Fig. 6.3, Chapter 6. The proper tolerances are easily maintained in smaller-sized components but some sacrifice must usually be made as the parts to be joined become larger in size.

Brazing Procedures

In general the handling of the cast irons during brazing is the same as for other base metals, assuming adequate preparation of the surfaces as outlined above. (See Chapter 9, Technique of Brazing.) It is well to bear in mind that the malleable, gray and ductile irons expand rather readily and that they conduct heat quite poorly. Thus the heating and cooling cycles deserve a great deal of consideration.

Postbraze Operations

The post braze operations, including the removal of excess flux are described in Chapter 10. Warm water is usually adequate for washing off the flux normally used with silver base filler metals. Inspection operations may then be made on the cleaned joints.

Typical Applications

Fig. 18.2 shows a steel sprocket brazed to a cast iron hub.

Fig. 18.3 shows an assembly of steel tubes brazed to a malleable iron header.

Fig. 18.4 shows several diesel engine subassemblies made of cast iron fittings brazed to steel tubing and Fig. 18.5 shows a tripod section made of steel tubing brazed to a cast iron base.

Fig. 18.6 shows the brazing of a malleable iron elbow in a steel piping system. BAg filler metal is being used.

Chapter 19

HEAT-RESISTANT ALLOYS

The term *heat resistant* is very broad and covers a wide field of base metals. Since the term is only relative, it can apply to a low-alloy steel having 2 per cent chromium, such as the type used in 1000 F boiler operation, or a high-cobalt alloy which operates at 1500F in an aircraft gas turbine. In general the low- and medium-alloy steels are used for maximum service temperatures ranging from 800 to 1100 F. Straight chromium steels are useful to 1200 F and austenitic alloys and so-called *super alloys* (cobalt bearing) are useful for applications up to 2000 F.

Design

In all metals the maximum load carrying ability drops as the temperature is increased and the time at service temperature is increased. Therefore, of prime importance in any assembly is the selection of the proper base metal to withstand the heat and corrosion conditions which are associated with high temperature operation. Appendix A covers the properties of some of the more common base metals.

The field of high temperature metallurgy is advancing so rapidly that it is impossible to include all of the specific data on the various alloys which are being developed for use above 1200 F. It is, therefore, recommended that specific design data be obtained from the manufacturers of heat-resistant alloys.

The design of a brazed joint for high temperature operation is the same as for other brazing applications for which basic information can be found in Chapter 6. It should be pointed out again that the operating temperature, stress in the joint, type of atmosphere or corrosive media and length of service will all be important factors in obtaining a satisfactory brazed assembly.

Brazing Filler Metals

Silver Alloys (BAg). Silver alloys are useful in applications where the unit stress in the joint is relatively low and temperatures during service do not exceed 800 F. If it is necessary to highly stress the brazed assembly or to assure a very long service life, the maximum operating temperature must be reduced. If the maximum operating temperature cannot be reduced, it is necessary to select a more suitable brazing filler metal. Data for the selection of the maximum operating stress for a given temperature and service life can best be obtained by conducting stress rupture tests as close to service conditions as possible.

Careful consideration should be given to oxidation of the brazing filler metal in the joint, as such oxidation may occur both at the surface of the joint and internally.

Copper (BCu). Pure copper finds some application in high temperature service but its use is limited by its low oxidation resistance. The useful temperature ranges are the same as for the silver alloys (BAg). Of the various commercial coppers available, oxygen-free copper shows the highest joint strength. Electrolytic copper is also used with satisfactory results. Phosphorus-deoxidized copper is not recommended for stainless steel.

Published data for type 403 stainless steel butt joints brazed with oxygen-free copper, hardened and drawn to Rockwell C 30–34 show the following stress rupture properties at 932 F:

10 hrs	23,000 psi
100 hrs	15,000 psi
1,000 hrs	8,000 psi
10,000 hrs	4,000 psi

The above data was for zero clearance at brazing temperature and an increase in clearance measurably reduces these values. For example, a clearance of 0.003 in. will drop the stress rupture value at 100 hours to 9,000 psi. Likewise as the test temperature increases the load carrying ability drops off very fast. See Fig. 19.1. The above data is for one set of conditions and one base metal in one laboratory and serves only to indicate the effect that temperature and time have on oxygen-free copper.

Short time tensile properties for butt brazed AMS 5770 (S-590) using oxygen-free copper and brazed in a pure dry hydrogen atmosphere are given in Fig. 19.2 and shear data is given in Fig. 19.3.

Silver Manganese (BAgMn). Silver manganese filler metal has found use up to 1200 F service temperature when loads are light; however, oxidation resistance is poor above 900 F. As in all high temperature service, the stress rupture, creep properties and service conditions must be carefully evaluated and tested prior to putting assemblies into service.

Joints brazed with BAgMn filler metal can be made by torch, induction or furnace brazing when flux is used. Brazing can be accomplished without the use of flux in dissociated ammonia or pure dry hydrogen if the temperature of brazing is sufficiently high and the atmosphere is sufficiently dry. See Fig. 19.2 and 19.3 for typical short time butt tensile and shear data.

Nickel-Chromium (BNiCr). This type of filler metal is especially useful because it has satisfactory physical and mechanical properties and

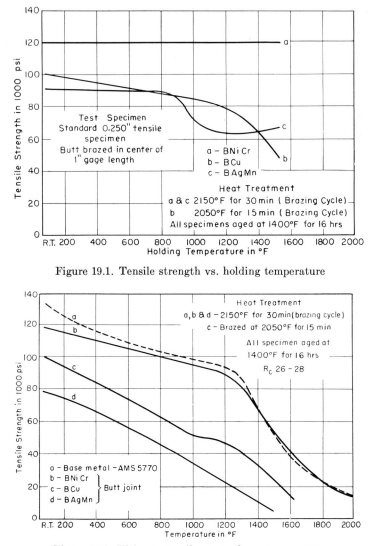

Figure 19.1. Tensile strength vs. holding temperature

Figure 19.2. Ultimate tensile strength vs. temperature

good oxidation resistance up through 2000 F. Again, it is necessary to have operating unit stress data before the maximum operating temperature can be determined for any specific design and set of service conditions.

Typical data on this class of brazing filler metal shows high strength at room temperature and at elevated temperatures when used to braze the following base metals: AISI type 347 (AMS 5646) stainless steel (Fig. 19.4) and S-590 (AMS 5770) cobalt stainless steel (Fig. 19.3) and AISI type 431

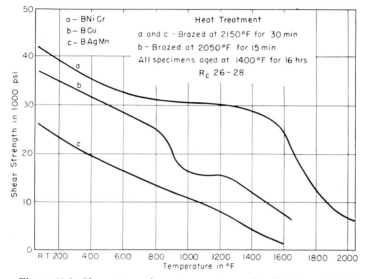

Figure 19.3. Shear strength vs. temperature. (Double Shear Joint)

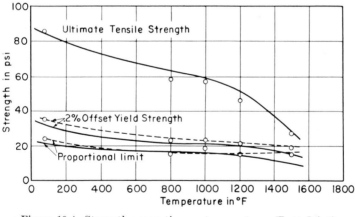

Figure 19.4. Strength properties vs. temperature. (Butt Joint)
- - - Base Metal
—O— BNiCr brazed
Heat treatment 2150° F. for 30 min. R_b 74–76

(AMS 5628) stainless steel (Fig. 19.5). See Appendix A for analyses of these metals. It should be noted that the first two base metals are austenitic and their brazed tensile strengths are equal to or nearly equal to their base metal strengths. The last base metal (type 431) is a martensitic type and can be hardened over a wide range. Fig. 19.5 shows the results of two hardness levels of base metal in butt brazed and base metal specimens.

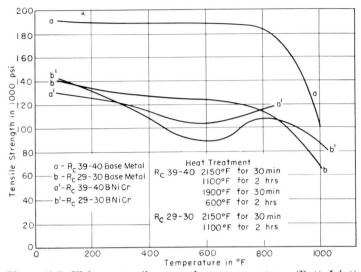

Figure 19.5. Ultimate tensile strength vs. temperature. (Butt Joint)

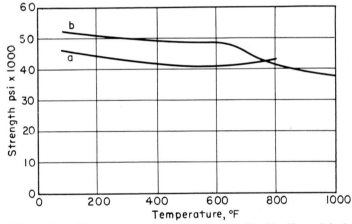

Figure 19.6. Shear strength vs. temperature. (Double Shear Joint)
a—2150° F for 30 min (brazing cycle); 600° F for 2 hr (temper); R_c 39-40
b—2150° F for 30 min (brazing cycle); 1100° F for 2 hr (temper); R_c 30-31

Fig. 19.3 and Fig. 19.6 show typical shear strength data for this class of brazing filler metals on S-590 and type 431 base metals. Again, Fig. 19.6 shows the variation in strength (shear) between two hardness levels.

Fig. 19.7 shows typical stress rupture data for the BNiCr brazing filler metal both in butt tension (curve *b*) and in shear (curve *c*). It should be pointed out that each base metal will have a different brazed strength and these data are not applicable to other base metals or other conditions of heat treatment.

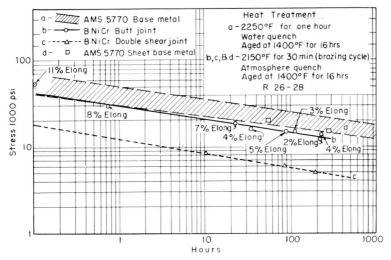

Figure 19.7. Stress rupture data for BNiCr brazed AMS 5770 at 1500° F

Other Filler Metals. The above listed brazing filler metals are the most commonly used. However, many special purpose filler metals have been and are being developed to satisfy new specific service requirements.

Brazing Procedure

Precleaning and Surface Preparation. The presence of chromium is common to essentially all base metals used as heat-resistant alloys. This requires that special attention be given to the removal of its oxides since they are of a refractory nature. Chemical cleaning, grinding and blasting are employed to remove these oxides. Other mechanical methods of cleaning such as wire brushing, scraping, etc., are not recommended. Blast cleaning must be used with caution. Many blasting materials such as alumina, silica sand, carbides, zirconite, etc., are nonmetallic materials and become embedded in the base metal being blasted. This forms a nonmetallic inclusion which lowers the strength of the brazed joint. Some blasting materials such as zirconite (zirconium oxide) entirely prevent the wetting and flow of the brazing filler metal.

Both precision and sand castings should be given special consideration in the cleaning cycle. All refractory materials used in the casting process must be removed before a satisfactory brazed joint can be produced. Mechanical or chemical removal of the contaminated surface layer is recommended. It is not uncommon to encounter cast alloys and carbides which have surface contamination. It causes *balling up* or lack of flow in the brazing filler metal. This surface contamination is most apparent when brazing is done in a controlled atmosphere furnace and a flux is not used.

For general information on cleaning, refer to Chapter 7. Additional information can also be found in Chapter 20 on Nickel and Nickel Alloys. This latter chapter includes information and formulas for pickling nickel alloys.

Fluxes and Atmospheres. Fluxes are generally applied in conjunction with torch, induction and resistance brazing using a silver alloy filler metal. When furnace brazing using combusted city gas as an atmosphere, base metals containing in excess of 0.5 per cent chromium require a flux to facilitate flow of the brazing filler metal. This covers practically all of the heat-resistant alloys since chromium is one of the major alloying elements used to impart heat-resistant properties.

Heat-resistant alloys can be brazed without the use of flux if a pure dry hydrogen or dissociated ammonia atmosphere is employed in a furnace. With proper control of the dew point and sufficiently high temperatures these atmospheres will reduce chromium oxide. BNiCr filler metal requires the use of pure dry hydrogen as even small amounts of nitrogen will cause nitriding with subsequent lack of melting and flow. For general information on atmospheres, refer to Chapter 4.

Alloying elements in the base metal put some limitations on the use of dissociated ammonia and pure dry hydrogen atmospheres. For example, aluminum, titanium, zirconium, and similar elements high on the electromotive series produce oxides which will not reduce even in very dry atmospheres. The presence of these elements is usually not detrimental when they are held below 0.5 per cent. In brazing Type 321 stainless steel with BCu filler metal, the titanium is leached out by the copper producing an alloy which is readily oxidized and will not satisfactorily flow or wet the stainless steel. BNiCr filler metal is unaffected by the titanium in Type 321 stainless steel but will not readily wet and flow on alloys having 2 and 3 per cent titanium. The difficulties encountered with these alloying elements can be handled in two different ways. The best method is to employ a protective surface layer such as nickel plating; this procedure allows the brazing to be accomplished in an atmosphere furnace without the use of flux, thus assuring higher quality brazing. The second method is to employ a small quantity of flux with the reducing atmosphere to facilitate wetting and flow of the brazing filler metal.

Postbraze Operations

Cleaning. In brazing heat-resistant metals, sometimes flux cannot be completely removed by hot water. In such cases a mechanical or chemical means must be used (see Chapter 10). Blasting, molten salt baths and other chemical baths are a few of the methods used. In any case a hot water rinse should be used after a chemical solution cleaning.

It is especially important that fluxes be removed from assemblies opera-

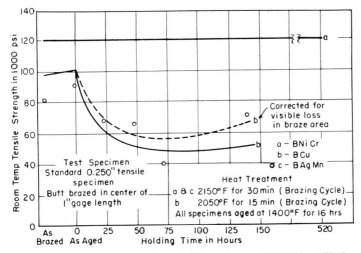

Figure 19.8. Tensile strength vs. holding time at 1500° F in still air

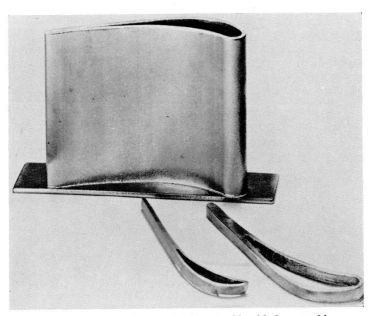

Figure 19.9. Stainless steel hollow turbine blade assembly

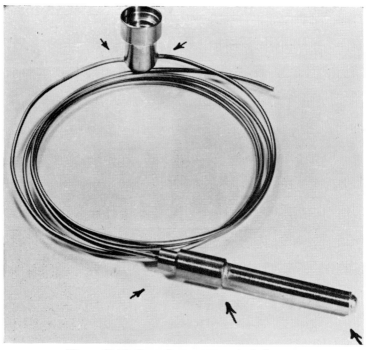

Figure 19.10. Brazed mercury control element

Figure 19.11. Type 347 stainless steel heat exchanger assembly

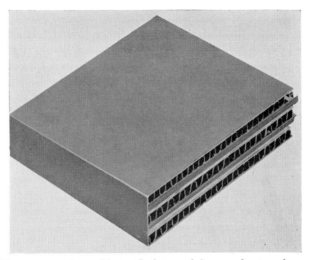

Figure 19.12. Brazed inconel plate and fin type heat exchanger

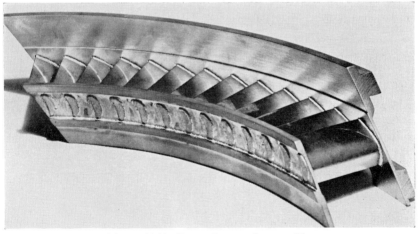

Figure 19.13. Jet engine nozzle assembly

ting at or above the melting temperature of the flux to avoid fluoride attack on the base metals.

Brazing operations done in a controlled atmosphere without flux do not require postbraze cleaning.

Heat Treatment. To obtain the required mechanical properties of the base metal, it is often necessary to heat treat an assembly subsequent to brazing. Low-alloy steel hardening may be accomplished by quenching and drawing while some of the high-alloy base metals obtain their properties by age hardening. Care should be exercised in selecting the brazing filler metal so it will not remelt or oxidize severely during the hardening cycle and it will be able to withstand the quenching rate. For additional information refer to Chapter 10.

Depending largely on the type of equipment used and the cooling rates obtainable, carbide precipitation may be present in stainless steels such as the 18-8 unstabilized grades. To prevent precipitation the assembly should be cooled rapidly or quenched fom the brazing temperature. This is usually not practical and it may, therefore, become necessary to reheat treat and quench the assembly to put the carbides back in solution. See Chapter 2, also Chapter 16.

Fig. 19.8 shows the effect of heat treatment at 1500 F on the tensile strength of AMS 5770 stainless steel brazed joints. Tests were conducted at room temperature.

Typical Applications

Fig. 19.9 shows a hollow turbine blade assembly in which the stainless steel parts were brazed with BNiCr filler metal.

Fig. 19.10 shows a Type 347 mercury control element 0.032 in. thick. Five brazes (shown by arrows) were made in one operation using BNiCr filler metal.

Fig. 19.11 shows a Type 347 stainless steel heat exchanger assembly in which the tube and sheet were brazed together.

Fig. 19.12 shows a plate and fin type heat exchanger assembly. The Inconel parts were brazed together.

Fig. 19.13 shows a jet engine nozzle section of Type 330 stainless and HS21 blades.

Chapter 20

NICKEL AND HIGH-NICKEL ALLOYS

Nickel and high-nickel alloys can readily be joined by most of the commonly-used brazing processes. Certain changes in procedures will be required, however, due to the different chemical, mechanical and physical properties of the alloys being joined. These properties will be found in Appendix A.

APPLICATIONS AND SERVICE REQUIREMENTS

Nickel and the high-nickel alloys are used principally where their high resistance to attack by many aqueous corrosive media and by many atmospheres at elevated temperatures is of particular advantage. In the selection of a brazing procedure it is important to determine the effect of service requirements on the brazed joints.

There are very few, if any, general statements regarding corrosion of nickel alloys in aqueous solutions or service at elevated temperatures which can be valid for all circumstances. It is better, therefore, to determine the suitability of the alloys by actual or simulated service tests. Some limitations on service at elevated temperatures are mentioned in succeeding paragraphs dealing with specific brazing filler metals.

BRAZING NICKEL ALLOYS

Cleanliness

Surface Pretreatment. The usual requirements for precleaning and surface preparation, outlined in Chapter 7, apply for the nickel alloys. In this instance, however, wire brushing is not satisfactory since the oxide films formed on nickel alloys are tenacious and will not be removed by this method. The pickling procedures recommended for these alloys are given in Table 20.1. It is good practice to clean parts just prior to brazing and in any case not allow them to stand more than 24 hours before brazing. Therefore, it is desirable to incorporate a cleaning requirement in the brazing procedure and to adhere to this procedure.

Sulfur Embrittlement. Nickel and high nickel alloys are subject to attack by sulfur at elevated temperatures. (see Chapter 2.) All materials which might contain sulfur, such as oil, grease, paint, marking pencil marks, lubricants and other materials must be removed from the part

141

TABLE 20.1. PICKLING RECOMMENDATIONS FOR NICKEL AND HIGH-NICKEL ALLOYS[a]
Formula to be used for the following types of Oxides

Base Metal	Light Tarnish	Reduced Oxide	Heavy Oxide
Nickel	3	4	5[c] and 3[b]
Duranickel	3	4	5[c] and 3[b]
Monel	1 and 2[b]	4	5 and 6[b]
"K" Monel	1 and 2[b]	4	5 and 6[b]
Inconel	—	—	7
Inconel "X"	—	—	7 or 7A

Make-up of Formulas

Formula #	#1	#2	#3	#4	#5	#6	#7	#7A
Water............gal.	1	1	1	1	1	1	1	3
Nitric acid (38° Bé)....qt.	4	4	9	—	—	—	4	4
Sulfuric acid (66° Bé)....pt.	—	—	12	¾	—	¾	—	—
Hydrochloric acid (20° Bé)....qt.	—	—	—	—	2	—	—	—
Hydrofluoric acid (40%)....pt.	—	—	¼[d]	—	—	—	1¼	1¼
Sodium chloride....lb.	½–¾	—	—	1	—	—	—	—
Sodium nitrate (Crude)....lb.	—	—	—	½	—	—	—	—
Sodium dichromate....lb.	—	—	—	—	—	1.1	—	—
Cupric chloride....lb.	—	—	—	—	¼	—	—	—
Temperature (F)	70–100	70–100	70–100	180–190 min.	180	70–100	70–100	120–140
Time	Not over 5 sec.	Not over 5 sec.	5–20 sec.	30–90 min.	20–40 min.	5–10 min.	15–90 min.	15–90 min.
Container Materials	Crocks, glass, ceramic	Stainless, glass, ceramic	Crocks, glass, ceramic	Crocks, glass, ceramic	Crocks, glass, ceramic, brick	Crocks, glass, ceramic, rubber	Carbon, brick	Carbon, brick

[a] All work should be degreased prior to pickling, and should be neutralized as a last operation in a 1–2% (vol.) ammonia solution.
[b] Hot water (180 F) rinse between dips.
[c] Will require 1 to 2 hours.
[d] Allow to cool before adding salt.
Safety Note: Fumes from these pickle solutions are strongly irritant. Ventilating hoods should be employed. (see Chapter 23)

prior to heating for brazing. In addition, the atmosphere used for heating must be relatively sulfur free. City gas, if used, should contain less than 20 grains of sulfur per 100 cubic feet. Oil, if used, should contain less than 0.5 per cent sulfur (No. 1 Fuel Oil).

Low-Melting Metals. Lead, bismuth, antimony and several other low-melting metals will attack the high-nickel alloys at elevated temperatures in much the same manner as sulfur. It is important that these metals or compounds which might contain these metals, such as threading compounds, be completely removed prior to brazing.

Stress-Corrosion Cracking

The high-nickel alloys, like other metals having high annealing temperatures, are subject to stress-corrosion cracking in the presence of molten brazing filler metals. Brazing should be done on annealed temper material only and the assembly should be stress-free during brazing. See Chapter 2 and the following paragraph.

Age-Hardenable Alloys

The age-hardenable high-nickel alloys, "Duranickel", "K" Monel, Inconel "X" and Inconel "W" are very susceptible to stress-corrosion cracking. These alloys should be brazed in the annealed or solution-treated condition with a relatively high melting brazing filler metal (preferably above 1600 F) that has sufficient strength to withstand handling during the age-hardening temperatures of 1100 F for "Duranickel" and "K" Monel and 1300 F for Inconel "X" and Inconel "W".

BRAZING FILLER METALS

Nickel and all high-nickel alloys melt above 2300 F; therefore, any of the brazing filler metals normally used for ferrous materials may be used in joining these alloys. The phosphorus-containing alloys in the BCuP classifications should not be used since a brittle phosphide is formed at the junction of the filler metal and the nickel-alloy base metal (Chapter 2.) The aluminum and magnesium base filler metals are not useful since a brittle alloy is formed.

Silver (BAg) Filler Metals

The BAg brazing filler metals may be used to join nickel and high-nickel alloys to themselves or to many other metals and alloys, other than aluminum and magnesium and their alloys. When properly applied, the joints will develop the full strength of annealed base material.

Filler Metal Selection. The lower melting filler metals, BAg-1 and BAg-2, are commonly used. For corrosive environments, however, alloys containing at least 50 per cent silver are preferred. BAg-7 is useful where stress-corrosion cracking might occur. BAg-9 is a good color match to the white materials such as nickel, Monel and Inconel; however, in service it will oxidize differently than the base metal and will be noticeably different in color in the oxidized condition.

Brazing Procedures. In general, the brazing procedures outlined in Chapters 1 through 11 apply. The joint clearance should be maintained between 0.002 and 0.005 in., when flux is used. For brazing in a controlled atmosphere, clearances as low as 0.0005 may be used. Lower joint strengths will result from wider clearances. AWS Type 3 fluxes are suitable on most alloys not containing aluminum. An AWS Type 4 flux may be used with aluminum-containing materials such as "K" Monel, "Duranickel" and Inconel "X". (See Chapter 4.) *The use of borax as a flux when brazing the high-nickel alloys with BAg filler metal is not recommended.* Borax does not melt at a low enough temperature and has other undesirable characteristics.

Any brazing process may be employed. In torch brazing, a large, soft, reducing flame is preferred. Salt-bath dip brazing may be employed but is seldom applied to nickel and nickel alloys. Metal-bath dip brazing finds limited application in brazing fine wire and small parts. If oxidation occurs during brazing, a pickling operation may be required to clean the assembly. Sometimes an anodic treatment in 25 per cent sulfuric acid is helpful for postbraze cleaning.

Copper (BCu) Filler Metal

The high-nickel alloys are capable of being brazed with BCu filler metal using the same equipment as used for steels with only minor changes in the brazing procedure due to the different characteristics of these alloys.

BCu filler metal will alloy more rapidly with nickel alloys than it does with steel. Therefore, copper will not flow as far before it has picked up enough nickel to raise its liquidus and reduce its fluidity. The filler metal should be placed as close to the joint as possible and there should be a sufficient reservoir to fill the joint. If too much copper is present and the excess flows over a thin member, it may perforate the thin member in a manner similar to the erosion of soil by water.

Elements such as chromium, aluminum and titanium form very refractory oxides which are not reduced in the normal furnace atmosphere. Therefore, "K" Monel, Inconel and Inconel "X" are more difficult to braze than Monel and nickel. Some procedure is necessary, either to prevent the formation of oxide or to flux away any oxide formed during heating. There are three methods of handling such a situation, as follows:

(1) The parts may be copper plated to prevent the formation of harmful oxides. The plating procedure is somewhat special in that oxides must not

be present on the surface of the parts under the plating. This can be accomplished by cleaning thoroughly by the usual procedure, using a reverse current strike in a nickel chloride bath followed by copper plating in the usual manner. About 0.0003 in. of copper is desired. This copper will prevent the formation of oxides, and in addition, will become part of the brazing filler metal.

(2) A flux may be employed to dissolve the oxides. Any flux suitable for welding these alloys may be used for this purpose. Due to the elevated temperatures any flux will become glass-like after cooling and relatively insoluble in any liquid medium. Quenching from an intermediate temperature will remove much flux by thermal shock. (See Chapter 10.) The best method of flux removal is by sand-blasting, chipping or grinding.

(3) A very dry furnace atmosphere (dew point −40 F or below) of dissociated ammonia or hydrogen will prevent chromium oxide from forming in the furnace and will reduce what little is left after cleaning.

Furnace and Atmospheres. Brazing with BCu filler metal is usually limited to furnace applications because of the atmosphere requirements. Heating may be with electricity, gas or oil, as long as the atmosphere can be maintained within desired limits. Standard reducing atmospheres of combusted city gas (AWS Atmosphere Type 1 or 2), dissociated ammonia (AWS Atmosphere Type 5) or hydrogen (AWS Atmosphere Type 6) may be used to braze Monel or nickel. Dry hydrogen (AWS Atmosphere Type 7) or dry dissociated ammonia is necessary to reduce chromium oxide at temperatures required for brazing Inconel with BCu filler metal. Inconel "X" and Inconel "W" will give difficulty even in a dry hydrogen atmosphere because of the presence of aluminum and titanium oxides. These alloys should be brazed with fluxes as well as reducing atmospheres.

Special Surface Treatment. A slightly-rough or lightly-etched surface presents better conditions for the capillary flow of the copper filler metal. Such surfaces will be wet for relatively great distances whereas polished surfaces will resist the flow of the copper filler metal.

Brazing Procedures. The design for brazing the nickel alloys with BCu filler metal is similar in many respects to the design for the brazing of steel. The tolerances for assembly range between a light press fit to 0.002 in. maximum clearance. The joint strength varies inversely with the joint clearance as discussed in Chapter 6. Brazed butt joints will provide strengths approaching those of the annealed base metals if proper clearances are maintained.

Most nickel alloy assemblies brazed with BCu filler metal require no postbraze treatment since they are usually bright as removed from the furnace. If desired, excess copper can be removed in a cold bath of 20 parts of household ammonia and one part hydrogen peroxide or a solution of 15 gallons of water, 1 gallon of sulfuric acid, and 80 pounds of chromic acid thoroughly mixed and used at room temperature. The length of time required depends on the thickness of copper to be removed.

Heat-Resistant Filler Metal

BNiCr brazing filler metal shows promise for applications requiring heat and corrosion resistance. Its excellent corrosion resistance compares with that of Inconel and its strength at elevated temperatures is far superior to that obtained with BAgMn or BCu filler metals. BNiCr contains boron which, at the brazing temperature, diffuses into the base metal, while the base metal diffuses into the brazing filler metal. This inter-diffusion raises the solidus of the filler metal, with the result that joints cannot be re-melted much below 2500 F, thus permitting service above the original solidus of the BNiCr filler metal.

BNiCr filler metal can be used with nickel, Monel Inconel and their age-hardenable variations.

Furnace Atmosphere. The atmosphere in the furnace recommended for brazing with BNiCr filler metal is dry hydrogen with a dew point below -50 F, and preferably about -100 F. Dry hydrogen at 2100 F will reduce the oxides of most metals except aluminum and titanium. When alloys containing appreciable quantities of aluminum or titanium, such as Inconel "X", are to be brazed, a flux must be used to reduce these oxides. Nickel plating, at least 0.0005 in. thick, has also been used effectively.

Brazing Processes. Because of the stringent atmosphere conditions, brazing is usually done in bell-type furnaces. A standard brazing furnace can be employed for heating if a special retort is built to contain the work and the low dew point hydrogen atmosphere. In this instance, an atmosphere of combusted city gas or dissociated ammonia may be used to surround the retort and protect the heating elements but it must not come in contact with the joint being brazed.

The details of construction of the retort require special attention. There should be a slight positive pressure in the retort to prevent mixing of air or the furnace atmosphere with the dry hydrogen in the retort. Seals employing alumina instead of silica have been used successfully. Silica would be reduced by dry hydrogen producing moisture. Mechanical seals have also been satisfactorily employed.

The retort must be carefully and thoroughly purged of all air prior to insertion in the furnace or an explosion may result.

Brazing Procedure. The design for brazing with BNiCr filler metal follows the same general requirements as for the BAg filler metals. The joint clearance should be maintained between 0.002 and 0.005 inch. Sufficient filler metal should be present to completely fill the crevice and form

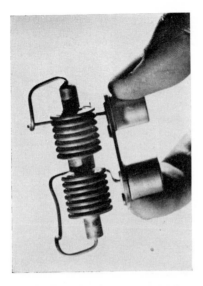

Figure 20.1. Inconel bellows containing 30 brazed joints

Figure 20.2. Inconel air-to-air heat exchanger assembly

fillets, avoiding excess filler metal since it may flow over surfaces by gravity and erode the base metal. Application temperatures range from 1900 to 2150 F. BNiCr powder is commonly used. It may be used directly in this form in holes or wells adjacent to joints, or it may be mixed with a vehicle for application by brush, spray or extrusion. A special vehicle is available which completely disappears upon heating, leaving no harmful residue to adversely affect brazing. The filler metal is also available as wire or ribbon, being powder, in a plastic vehicle.

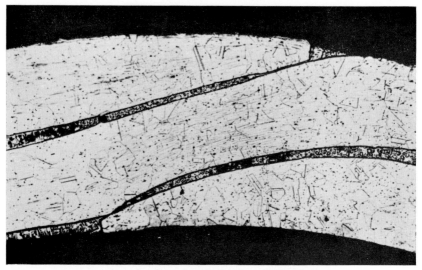

Section of typical tube at lap

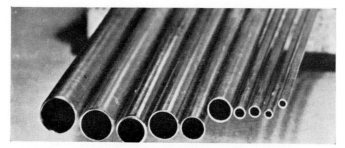

Figure 20.3. Monel tubing made by furnace brazing

For most applications no postbraze treatment is required. However, if flux has been used, a flux removal operation is necessary. This will be best done mechanically by grinding, chipping or sand blasting. (see Chapter 10.)

The inspection requirements of material for high temperature service will be more rigid because the quality of the brazed joint must be maintained at a high level.

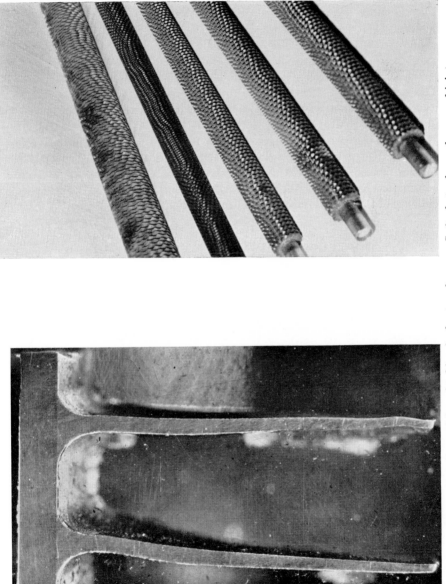

Figure 20.4. Inconel finned tubing for heat exchangers. Left photo shows close-up of joint.

Typical Applications

Fig. 20.1 shows an assembly of Inconel bellows used in a pressure gage The assembly involved 30 joints brazed with BAg filler metal, and must withstand 750 psi test pressure.

Fig. 20.2 shows a section of an air-to-air heat exchanger fabricated from 0.015 in. Inconel using BNiCr filler metal.

Fig. 20.3 shows varying sizes of tubing formed from spiral lapped Monel. The strip is plated with BCu filler metal, coiled and then run through a hydrogen-atmosphere furnace. The top view shows a section of the tubing at the brazed joint.

Fig. 20.4 shows some samples of Inconel finned tubing used for heat exchangers. The fins are strip Inconel, edge coiled around the tubing and furnace brazed using BNiCr filler metal. Tubes of this type have given satisfactory service at 1200 F for over 5000 hours. The left photo shows a close-up of the joint formed by the tube wall and fin edge.

Chapter 21

PRECIOUS METAL CONTACTS

While there are several important industrial applications for the precious metals it is only in the electrical contact field that there is any extensive use of brazing filler metals for joining them. Millions of contacts are required yearly as practically all types of electrical apparatus require some type of contact for opening and closing circuits. The contact is usually small and it must be attached to the equipment in some manner. The commonly accepted method for attachment is brazing.

The varying conditions under which electrical contacts are used demand a wide range of physical characteristics. Consequently a large number of precious metal alloys have been developed to meet this demand. Silver, gold and the platinum metals are used separately or in various alloy combinations. Silver, in particular, has been used for contacts in combination with other metals produced either by direct alloying or, as in the case of the more refractory metals, by powdered metal processes. The most commonly used metals are copper, zinc, cadmium, nickel, molybdenum, tungsten and iron. Also, various nonmetallic materials such as carbon and refractory oxides may be mixed with the silver. These nonmetallic materials are used to prevent sticking or fusing of the contacts in service. Since this property similarly adversely affects the flowing of the filler metal on the contact, it may introduce a difficult brazing problem. Silver is also subject to hydrogen embrittlement. (see Chapter 2).

Any of the standard silver (BAg) brazing filler metals may be used. As it is customary practice to preplace the filler metal, the form most generally used is thin strip, cut to conform to the shape of the contact. Powder or filings mixed with flux to form a paste which can be painted on the joint surfaces is also a convenient form to use. Contact materials, such as fine silver or silver-copper alloys, are also supplied with a thin layer of the filler metal alloyed on one side. This form saves considerable labor in assembling large numbers of small contacts.

The major portion of the electrical contacts are small in size and have to be brazed to some type of holder or arm which may be either a ferrous or nonferrous alloy. The contacts are usually brazed on to a flat surface or a surface having the same contour as the contact. Thus, in general, the question of joint clearances, differences in thermal expansion and design of the

151

joint are of relatively minor importance. Resistance and furnace brazing are most widely used.

Resistance brazing is done either with a spot welding machine or a pair of carbon tongs in a portable gun. As the electrical contacts usually have a relatively high electrical conductivity it is preferable to use carbon or tungsten electrodes on the spot welding machine so that the heat required is developed directly in the electrodes and the contact assembly is heated by conduction. The time cycle for heating by this process is very short and the joint surfaces are protected from extensive oxidation. The flux should, therefore, be thin and watery. Dry fluxes or thick flux pastes are poor electrical conductors and will interfere with the passage of the current through the joint. When this occurs oxides form at the joint surfaces which prevent the flow of the filler metal.

Furnace brazing is usually done in controlled-atmosphere furnaces. Although fluxing the joints is recommended even in highly reducing atmospheres much of this type of work is done without the use of the flux because of the labor involved in fluxing large numbers of small assemblies and because the flux rapidly destroys the trays used to hold and jig the contacts. Since the brazing temperatures are below the temperature required for

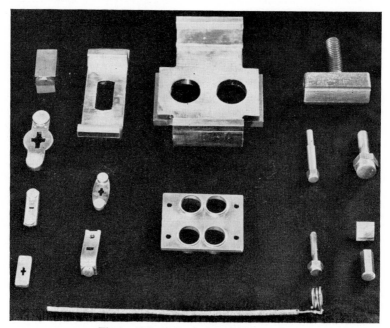

Figure 21.1. Brazed electrical contacts

efficient reduction of any oxide films which may be formed, successful braz-ing without flux requires a strongly reducing atmosphere with a low moisture content to prevent oxidation of the filler metal. This also means that particular care must be taken in precleaning in order to have all surfaces free from dirt or oxide prior to the brazing operation.

Most of the contact materials are readily brazed by the standard proce-dures, but in some cases special preparation of the surfaces is necessary. Graphite in silver-graphite mixtures may seriously interfere with brazing. Burning the graphite out of the joint surfaces by heating under oxidizing conditions before brazing is resorted to at times. When metallic oxides, such as cadmium oxide, are present, it may be necessary to chemically clean the surface to remove the oxides before brazing. Since contact ma-terials are usually made by powdered metal processes, it is possible to make the contacts to be brazed with a fine silver coating on the joint surface. Contacts high in molybdenum may require a special filler metal. In this instance, the addition of phosphorus to the filler metal has been found to be an effective means of obtaining satisfactory wetting of the base metal surface by the filler metal.

As it is not possible to cover all the combinations of this type here the supplier of contacts should be consulted regarding the best procedures for brazing these special cases.

Typical Applications

Fig. 21.1 shows a representative group of brazed contacts.

Chapter 22

OTHER METALS

In addition to the more commonly used metals described in previous chapters, there are other metals such as the hard carbides, tungsten, titanium, tantalum, molybdenum, zirconium, etc., which are used for special applications or which are relatively new to industry. With the exception of the hard carbides, published information on the brazing of these materials is rather sparse. Where use of any of these metals is contemplated it may be necessary to develop suitable brazing procedures based on the metallurgical properties of the material and its intended use. The suppliers of these materials may be helpful.

The hard carbides are widely used as cutting materials, generally in relatively small sizes which must be attached to other base metals of some form. Mechanical methods for doing this are used but the preferred procedure is brazing.

Tungsten, molybdenum, tantalum and other refractory metals are used as electrical contacts and as various tube components in the electron tube industry. A wide variety of uses is being developed for titanium and there are many instances where ability to braze it would be advantageous.

Hard Carbides

The hard carbides vary widely in composition and may contain any of several different refractory metals. While any of the BAg-1 through BAg-7 filler metals may be used, those which contain nickel (BAg-3 and -4) are generally preferred because nickel improves wettability. BCuZn-6 and BCuZn-7 are also widely used and are particularly recommended where heat treatment of the base metal after brazing is necessary. BAgMn and BCu filler metals alo have been extensively used for brazing carbides, especially where a postbraze heat treatment is required.

The basic rules of brazing as outlined in the other chapters apply equally to brazing carbides. Cleaning of the carbide is particularly important. Mechanical cleaning by grinding on a diamond or other refractory wheel is more effective than chemical methods. Type 3 flux (see Chapter 4) is recommended. Torch, induction and furnace brazing are commonly used. Furnace brazing is used, particularly for BCu filler metal.

Any of the usual forms of filler metal may be used but thin sheet inserts are preferable. On certain of the carbides it is difficult to wet the surface with the filler metal and in such cases it may be necessary to precoat the carbide by rubbing the molten filler metal over the surface with a steel rod or by preplating with copper or nickel. Wherever possible it is good practice to promote wetting of the carbide and minimize voids by inducing movement in the parts being brazed while the filler metal is molten.

Carbide will occasionally crack on cooling after brazing because of wide differences in thermal expansion of the carbide and the metals to which it may be joined. This may be overcome by use of a *sandwich* braze, i.e., the insertion of a shim of a soft metal which is brazed on one side to the carbide and on the other to the other base metal. This soft metal will creep during the cooling and reduce the stress in the joint. Copper or nickel are suitable metals for this purpose. A special brazing sheet is available for making sandwich brazes. This consists of a copper core clad on both sides with a thin layer of nickel-bearing BAg filler metal.

Tungsten

Thorough cleaning of the tungsten just prior to brazing is essential. This can be accomplished mechanically or by immersion in a warm 50/50 solution of nitric and hydrofluoric acids for a few seconds followed by rinsing in hot water and alcohol. Sodium hydride baths (700 F), followed by the standard procedure which includes a water quench, water rinse, acid dip and water rinse are also used for the cleaning operations. A hot concentrated solution of sodium hydroxide is suitable for cleaning tungsten. A dilute solution of sodium nitrite used electrolytically with ac is also suitable.

Filler metals for brazing tungsten are: nickel, nickel-copper, copper-nickel, gold, copper, gold-copper, gold-silver-platinum alloys, or the like. Such brazing filler metals are also satisfactory for vacuum tube applications. (See Chapter 2—Vapor Pressure.)

Where the tungsten joint is to be incandescent in use, brazing should not be employed since the alloying of gold or nickel with tungsten lowers the solidus of the tungsten alloy formed and may cause failure of the joint.

Molybdenum

BAg-8 filler metal is suitable for furnace brazing molybdenum in a controlled atmosphere in addition to the filler metals listed above for tungsten. Modifications of the BAg filler metals containing small percentages of phosphorus have been developed and have proved successful for torch brazing. For these modifications it is advisable to contact the suppliers of filler metal.

Rhodium and mixtures of cobalt and nickel powders are also used for brazing molybdenum. Another acceptable practice is to paint the parts with a paste of fine nickel powder and sinter the nickel to the molybdenum prior to brazing. Torch brazing of molybdenum using an oxy-hydrogen flame and a nickel filler metal has been successful.

Tantalum

A heavy plating of nickel or platinum is used for vacuum brazing or resistance brazing under water. Tantalum forms a homogeneous solid solution with nickel up to a tantalum content of 36 per cent and the liquidus falls smoothly from 2640 to 2460 F (1450 to 1350 C). Junctions between tantalum and nickel should thus be avoided when service temperatures are to exceed 1830 F (1000 C).

In general the formation of brittle intermetallic compounds, such as Ni_3Ta in brazed joints should be watched carefully. Copper-gold alloys containing substantially less than 40 per cent gold (BCuAu-2 for example) are recommended as filler metals. Copper-gold alloys, containing between 40 and 90 per cent gold, tend to form age-hardening compounds which also are brittle.

Tantalum has also been brazed with some BAg filler metals with the use of an AWS Type 7 flux but these alloys are not recommended because of a tendency to embrittle the tantalum.

Titanium

Titanium may be brazed by torch, furnace, induction or resistance brazing. For torch brazing liberal quantities of AWS Type 6 flux should be used. Inert gases such as helium or argon are recommended for the other brazing processes. These gases as supplied may contain objectionable water vapor and, if so, may require drying. By removal of gases to a suitably low pressure (500 microns or less) titanium may be vacuum brazed with pure silver.

Titanium may be brazed with fine silver (Fig. 22.1) or with the BAg filler metals (Fig. 22.2). The time the base metal is in contact with the molten filler metal should be kept as short as possible. Otherwise the fine silver will completely diffuse into the titanium without brazing or the BAg alloys will form brittle compounds at the joint interfaces. Fine-silver lap joints having an ultimate shear strength in the order of 30,000 psi exhibit ductile fracture. By following carefully controlled brazing procedures, joints having tensile strengths of 40,000 to 60,000 psi may be obtained with the BAg alloys although such joints may have low ductility.

Brazing in a vacuum is suitable only for a limited type of work and it will be necessary to induction or furnace braze other types of work. For furnace brazing, vacuums of 10^{-5} or 10^{-6} millimeters of mercury are required. When heating time is appreciable, titanium will still show discoloration in a 10^{-4} vacuum.

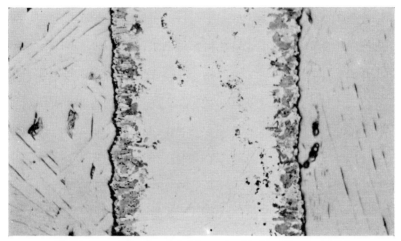

Figure 22.1. Titanium joint brazed with fine silver.—500×

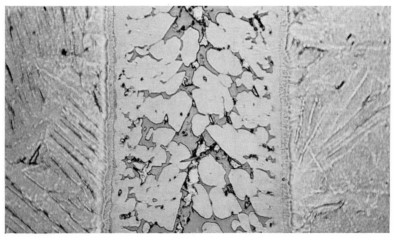

Figure 22.2. Titanium joint brazed with BAg-1a Filler Metal. (Etchant 20% HNO₃ + 20% HF + 60% Glycerine)—500×

Zirconium

Zirconium is difficult to braze. The lack of a suitable flux for removing the oxide film usually prevents easy brazing of zirconium or zirconium alloys by any of the simple techniques. After proper cleaning, sound joints can be made with the BAg filler metals, but the joints are usually brittle due to the formation of intermetallic compounds.

Zirconium can be brazed satisfactorily after coating with another metal.

Figure 22.3. Brazing carbide tip to steel shank

Zinc coating by immersion in a molten zinc chloride bath has been reported as one method for preparing zirconium for brazing.

The corrosion properties of brazed joints in zirconium are usually poor in comparison with the base metal.

Typical Applications

Fig. 22.3 shows a carbide tip being brazed to a steel shank. Radiant cup type air-gas burners and BAg filler metal are being used.

Chapter 23

SAFETY AND HEALTH PROTECTION

Most brazing operations do not involve any special hazards not common to other welding processes. The usual precautions dictated for the installation and use of the equipment and materials as specified in American Standard Z49, *Safety in Electric and Gas Welding and Cutting Operations*, published by American Welding Society should be followed.

Except for the special precautions required in the use of certain materials, as described below, normal ventilation meeting the requirement of American Standard Z49 is adequate.

Proper care should be taken in the handling of hot objects. Brazers should wear clothing, including shoes, which will afford the necessary protection against falling objects and heat. Goggles or spectacles, as necessary, should be used.

Some brazing filler metals contain toxic materials such as cadmium and beryllium; some fluxes contain fluorides and other fluorine compounds. The use of such filler metals or fluxes without harmful effects from the toxicity of these materials requires special precautions. The same precautions would apply whether welding or other hot work is done on previously brazed joints.

Cadmium

Cadmium is encountered as an element in some brazing filler metals; it may also be found as a base metal plating. The most important precaution is to avoid the inhalation of cadmium fumes, which are present in greater quantity when plated materials are brazed.

Where brazing operations involve cadmium-plated materials adequate local exhaust ventilation or individual air-supplied respirators must be provided. Brazing of such materials should not be done in confined spaces unless all workers present in such confined spaces during brazing operations are provided with individual air-supplied respirators.

For production brazing with cadmium-bearing filler metal, mechanical ventilation adequate to remove the fumes must be provided. For small, intermittent brazing operations with such filler metals natural ventilation may be adequate. Where brazing with cadmium-bearing filler metal is done

159

in a confined space, even intermittently, local exhaust ventilation or individual air-supply respirators are required.

Fluorides and Other Fluorine Compounds

These compounds are encountered in brazing fluxes, particularly those used with silver, magnesium and aluminum-silicon brazing filler metals. Toxic effects may be produced by the inhalation of fumes from these compounds or by the oral consumption of such fluorine-bearing materials.

The hazards may be overcome by the use of adequate ventilation and by observing rules of cleanliness to prevent the absorption of these compounds through the mouth or through skin openings such as cuts. All commonly available commercial fluxes containing fluorides or other fluorine compounds are labeled with a standard precaution formulated by the American Welding Society and reading as follows:

CAUTION

Contains Fluorides

This flux when heated gives off
fumes which may irritate eyes,
nose and throat.

Avoid fumes—use only in well-ventilated spaces.
Avoid contact of flux with eyes or skin.
Do not take internally.

The above instructions should be strictly followed.

Furnace brazing with fluorine-bearing fluxes requires regular exhaust of the fumes generated to prevent attack of exposed metals; the air changes necessary for this reason are also adequate from the standpoint of health protection.

Dip brazing with fluorine-bearing fluxes should be done in baths provided with a suitable exhaust.

Beryllium

Beryllium is occasionally used in magnesium filler metal for furnace brazing, and to an even lesser extent in aluminum brazing filler metal. Beryllium-copper base metal is also brazed. The presence of beryllium in any form requires adequate ventilation and cleanliness to avoid absorption of the material orally, through skin openings or by inhalation.

Zinc

Zinc, either as a base metal coating or as a base metal or filler metal constituent, may volatilize or oxidize and produce fumes which cause "zinc chills" or "zinc fume fever". Although the health hazard from zinc fumes is less serious than that of the above elements, adequate local exhaust ventilation must be provided.

Cleaning Compounds

It is imperative that proper ventilation be provided in areas where cleaning operations are being conducted. The use of carbon tetrachloride is not recommended. Its presence, even in small quantities, and at any temperature, is a serious cumulative health hazard. Trichloroethylene and tetrachloroethylene vapors, if in contact with a hot object or in the vicinity of an electric arc, become dissociated generating free halogens and phosgene which are toxic. The vapors of these cleaning solvents are heavier than air and can travel long distances from the cleaning vats.

Some solvents, such as benzene and gasoline, are flammable as well as toxic. While they are not used frequently because of this, proper protection against the possibility of fire must be taken when they are used.

Before using a chemical cleaner it is necessary to determine if any of its constituents are flammable or produce toxic fumes and the necessary precautions taken accordingly. Where practical, a hood with an exhaust system connected to it, located over the cleaning and pickling tank will effectively remove fumes.

Caution must be exercised in the handling and use of acids and alkalies.

Brazing Atmospheres

Mixtures of some furnace atmospheres and air are extremely explosive. Before heating a retort or furnace containing any such atmosphere below 1300 F, it is necessary to thoroughly purge all air. Carbon monoxide and the metal vapors occurring in brazing atmospheres are toxic. Adequate ventilation must be provided unless the exhaust gases and vapors are trapped and burned.

APPENDIX A

PROPERTIES OF BRAZEABLE METALS AND ALLOYS

Note: Yield strengths are reported for the .2 per cent offset method unless otherwise specified. Values suffixed YP, PL or .5 per cent signify yield point, proportional limit, or .5 per cent extension under load.

Hardness values are Brinell Hardness Numbers unless suffixed R_b or R_f (Rockwell B or Rockwell F).

Appendix A

Metal	Nominal Composition (%)	Condition and Temper	Yield Strength, 1000 psi	Tensile Strength, 1000 psi	Elongation in 2 in. (%)	Hardness	Density lb/in.³	Specific Gravity	Melting Range (°F)	Specific Heat (32–212°F) Btu/lb./°F	Coeff. Therm. Exp., (32–212°F) 10^{-6} in./in./°F	Thermal Conductivity, (room temp.) Btu/sq. ft./in./°F/hr.	Electrical Resistivity, (68°F) ohms/cir. mil ft.	Tensile Modulus of Elasticity, 10^6 psi
Aluminum 2S	Al 99+	Annealed -O	5	13	45	23	0.098	2.71	1190–1215	0.22	13.1	1540	17.6	9.9
		Cold worked⁵-H14	16	17.5	20	32								
		Cold worked¹-H18	22	24	15	44						1510	18.2	
Aluminum 3S	Al Bal. Mn 1.2	Annealed -O	6	16	40	28	0.099	2.73	1190–1210	0.22	12.9	1335	20.7	10
		Cold worked⁵-H14	19	21.5	16	40						1105	25.3	
		Cold worked¹-H18	26	29	10	55						1075	25.9	
Aluminum 4S	Al Bal. Mn 1.2 Mg 1.0	Annealed -O	10	26	25	45	0.098	2.72	1165–1205	0.22	13.3	1130	24.7	10
		Cold worked⁵-H34	27	34	12	63								
		Cold worked¹-H38	34	40	6	77								
Aluminum B50S	Al Bal. Mg 1.2	Annealed -O	8	21	24	36	0.097	2.69	1160–1205	0.22	13.2	1330	20.7	10
		Cold worked⁵-H34	24	27.5	8	50								
		Cold worked¹-H38	28	31	6	57								
Aluminum 52S	Al Bal. Mg 2.5 Cr 0.25	Annealed -O	12	27	30	45	0.097	2.68	1100–1200	0.22	13.2	958	29.6	10.1
		Cold worked⁵-H34	31	37	14	67								
		Cold worked¹-H38	36	41	8	85								

¹ Hard temper

⁵ Half hard temper

165

APPENDIX A (Continued)

Metal	Nominal Composition (%)		Condition and Temper	Yield Strength, 1000 psi	Tensile Strength, 1000 psi	Elongation in 2 in. (%)	Hardness	Density lb/in.³	Specific Gravity	Melting Range (°F)	Specific Heat (32°-212°) Btu/lb./°F	Coeff. Therm. Exp., (32-212°F) 10^{-6} in./in./°F	Thermal Conductivity, (room temp), Btu/hr./ft./in./°F	Electrical Resistivity, (68°F) ohms/cir. mil ft.	Tensile Modulus of Elasticity, 10^6 psi
Aluminum 53S	Al	Bal.	Annealed -O	8	16	35	26	0.097	2.69	1075–1205	0.22	13.1	1190	23.0	9.9
	Si	0.7	Heat treated[6]-T4	20	30	21	62						1075	25.9	
	Mg	1.3	Heat treated[7]-T5	27	21	15	60						1190	23.0	
	Cr	0.25	Heat treated[8]-T6	32	37	13	80						1075	25.9	
Aluminum 61S	Al	Bal.	Annealed -O	8	18	30	30	0.098	2.70	1080–1205	0.22	13.1	1190	23.0	9.9
	Cu	0.25	Heat treated[6]-T4	21	35	25	65						1075	25.9	
	Mg	1.0	Heat treated[8]-T6	40	45	17	95						1075	25.9	
	Cr	0.25													
	Si	0.6													
Aluminum 62S	Al	Bal.	Annealed -O	6.5	17	30	28	0.098	2.70	1080–1205	0.22	12.4	1190	23.0	9.9
	Cu	0.25	Heat treated[6]-T4	21	35	25	65						1070	23.0	
	Si	0.6	Heat treated[8]-T6	40	45	17	95						1070		
	Mg	1.0													
Aluminum 63S	Al	Bal.	Heat treated[6]-T42	13	22	20	42	0.098	2.70	1140–1205	0.22	13.0	1335	20.7	9.9
	Si	0.4	Heat treated[7]-T5	27	21	12	60						1450	18.8	
	Mg	0.7	Heat treated[8]-T6	31	35	12	73						1450	18.8	
Aluminum 43	Al	Bal.	Sand cast[2]	8	19	8	40	0.097	2.69	1065–1170	0.22	12.3	1015	28	10.3
	Si	5	Perm. mold cast	9	23	10	45								

Material	Composition		Condition												
Aluminum A612	Al Cu Mg Zn	Bal. 0.5 0.7 6.5	Sand cast²	25	35	5	75	0.102	2.81	1105–1195	0.22	13.4	957	29.6	10.3
Aluminum C612	Al Cu Mg Zn	Bal. 0.5 0.35 6.5	Perm. mold cast	18	35	8	70	0.103	2.84	1120–1190	0.22	13.1	1103	25.9	10.3
Copper, oxygen-free (OF)	Cu	99.92 Min.	0.050 mm anneal Cold rolled, hard Hot rolled	10(.5%) 45(") 10(")	32 50 34	45 6 45	40 Rf 90 " 45 "	0.321 to 0.323	8.89 to 8.94	1981	0.092	9.8	2762	10.3	17.0
Copper, electrolytic Tough Pitch (ETP)	Cu O	99.9+ 0.04	0.050 mm anneal Cold rolled, hard Hot rolled	10(") 45(") 10(")	32 50 34	45 6 45	40 " 90 " 45 "	0.321 to 0.323	8.89 to 8.94	1949–1981	0.092	9.8	2712	10.3	17.0
Copper, de-oxidized (DLP)	Cu P	99.9+ 0.02	0.050 mm anneal	10(")	32	45	40 "	0.323	8.94	1981	0.092	9.8	2352	12.2	17.0
Commercial bronze, 90%	Cu Zn	90 10	0.035 mm anneal ½ hard Hot rolled	12(") 45(") 10(")	38 52 37	50 15 45	57 " 58 Rb 53 Rf	0.318	8.80	1870–1910	0.09	10.2	1303	23.5	17.0

² As Cast
⁶ Solution heat treated
⁷ Artificially aged only
⁸ Solution heat treated, then artificially aged
Note: Lake copper (silver bearing, fire refined) has essentially the same properties as electrolytic tough pitch copper.

APPENDIX A (Continued)

Metal	Nominal Composition (%)		Condition and Temper	Yield Strength, 1000 psi	Tensile Strength, 1000 psi	Elongation in 2 in. (%)	Hardness	Density lb./in.³	Specific Gravity	Melting Range (°F)	Specific Heat (32°-212°F) Btu/lb./°F	Coeff. Therm. Exp., (32°-212°F) 10^{-6} in./in./°F	Thermal Conductivity, (room temp.) Btu/sq. ft./in./hr./°F	Electrical Resistivity, (68°F) ohms/cir. mil ft.	Tensile Modulus of Elasticity, 10^6 psi
Red brass, 85%	Cu	85	0.035 mm anneal	14 (.5%)	41	46	63 R_f	0.316	8.75	1810-1880	0.09	10.4	1104	28.0	17.0
	Zn	15	½ hard	49 (")	57	12	65 R_b								
Low brass, 80%	Cu	80	0.035 mm anneal	15 (")	46	48	66 R_f	0.313	8.67	1770-1830	0.09	10.6	972	32	16
	Zn	20	½ hard	50 (")	61	18	70 R_b								
Cartridge brass, 70%	Cu	70	0.025 mm anneal	19 (")	51	55	72 R_f	0.308	8.53	1680-1750	0.09	11.1	840	37.0	16.0
	Zn	30	¼ hard	40 (")	54	43	55 R_b								
			½ hard	52 (	62	23	70 "								
Yellow brass	Cu	65	0.025 mm anneal	19 (")	51	55	72 R_f	0.306	8.47	1660-1710	0.09	11.3	804	38	15.0
	Zn	35	½ hard	50 (")	61	23	70 R_b								
			Hard	60 (")	74	8	80 "								
Muntz metal	Cu	60	Hot rolled	21 (")	54	45	85 R_f	0.303	8.39	1650-1660	0.09	11.6	852	37	15.0
	Zn	40	Cold rolled (½ hard)	50 (")	70	10	75 R_b								
Low-leaded brass	Cu	65	½ hard	50 (")	61	23	70 "	0.306	8.47	1650-1700	0.09	11.3	804	40	15.0
	Pb	0.5													
	Zn	34.5													
Medium-leaded brass	Cu	65	½ hard	50 (")	61	21	70 "	0.306	8.47	1630-1700	0.09	11.3	804	40	15.0
	Pb	1.0													
	Zn	34													

168

Material	Composition	Condition												
High-leaded brass	Cu 65 / Pb 2.0 / Zn 33	½ hard	50 (.5%)	61	20	70 R$_b$	0.306	8.47	1630–1670	0.09	11.3	804	40	15.0
Leaded muntz metal	Cu 60 / Pb 0.6 / Zn 39.4	Hot rolled	20 (")	54	45	80 R$_f$	0.304	8.41	1630–1650	0.09	11.6	852	38	15.0
Inhibited admiralty	Cu 71 / Zn 28 / Sn 1	Hot rolled	18 (")	48	65	70 "	0.308	8.53	1650–1720	0.09	11.2	768	42	16.0
Aluminum brass	Cu 76 / Zn 22 / Al 2	0.025 mm anneal	27 (")	60	55	77 "	0.301	8.33	1710–1780	0.09	10.3	696	45	16
Naval brass	Cu 60 / Zn 39.25 / Sn 0.75	Light anneal	30 (")	63	40	60 R$_b$	0.304	8.41	1630–1650	0.09	11.8	804	40	15.0
		½ hard	53 (")	75	20	82 "								
		Hot rolled	25 (")	55	50	55 "								
Free-cutting brass	Cu 61.5 / Zn 35.5 / Pb 3	¼ hard (11%)	45 (")	56	20	62 "	0.307	8.50	1630–1650	0.09	11.4	804	40	14
Phosphor bronze, 5% (A)	Cu 95 / Sn 5	½ hard	55 (")	68	28	78 "	0.320	8.86	1750–1920	0.09	9.9	564	58	16
		Hard	75 (")	81	10	87 "								
Phosphor bronze, 8% (C)	Cu 92 / Sn 8	½ hard	55 (")	76	32	84 "	0.318	8.80	1620–1880	0.09	10.1	432	80	16
		Hard	72 (")	93	10	93 "								

Metal	Nominal Composition (%)	Condition and Temper	Yield Strength 1000 psi	Tensile Strength, 1000 psi	Elongation in 2 in. (%)	Hardness	Density lb./in.³	Specific Gravity	Melting Range (°F)	Specific Heat (32–212°F) Btu/lb./°F	Coeff. Therm. Exp., (32°–212°F) 10^{-6}	Thermal Conductivity, (room temp.) Btu/sq. ft./in./hr./°F	Electrical Resistivity, (68°F) ohms/cir. mil ft.	Tensile Modulus of Elasticity, 10^6 psi
Phosphor bronze, 10% (D)	Cu 90 Sn 10	½ hard Hard	— —	83 100	32 13	92 R_b 97 "	0.317	8.78	1550–1830	0.09	10.2	348	94	16
Phosphor Bronze, 1.25% (E)	Cu 98.75 Sn 1.25 P Trace	½ hard Hard	45 (.5%) 50 (")	55 65	16 8	64 " 75 "	0.321	8.89	1900–1970	0.09	9.9	1440	22	17
Cupro-nickel, 30%	Cu 70 Ni 30	Hot rolled	20 (")	55	45	35 "	0.323	8.94	2140–2260	0.09	9.0	204	225	22
Cupro-nickel, 10%	Cu 89 Ni 10 Fe 1	0.25 mm anneal Light drawn	15 (") 57 (")	45 60	40 12	65 R_f 72 R_b	0.323	8.94	2010–2090	0.09	9.3	312	90	18
Nickel silver, 65-18	Cu 65 Zn 17 Ni 18	0.035 mm anneal ½ hard Hard	25 (") 62 (") 74 (")	58 74 85	40 8 3	85 R_f 83 R_b 87 "	0.316	8.73	1960–2030	0.09	9.0	228	170	18
Nickel silver, 55-18	Cu 55 Zn 27 Ni 18	Hard	85 (")	100	3	91 "	0.314	8.70	1930	0.09	9.3	204	190	18

Material	Composition		Condition												
Nickel silver, 65-15	Cu	65	0.050 mm anneal	19(.5%)	55	42	73 R$_f$	0.314	8.70	1970	0.09	9.0	252	150	18
	Zn	20	½ hard	62(")	74	10	80 R$_b$ "								
	Ni	15	Hard	75(")	85	3	87 "								
Nickel silver, 65-12	Cu	65	0.050 mm anneal	19( )	54	45	73 R$_f$	0.314	8.69	1900	0.09	9.0	276	130	18
	Zn	23	½ hard	60( )	73	11	80 R$_b$ "								
	Ni	12	Hard	75( )	85	4	89 "								
Nickel silver, 65-10	Cu	65	0.050 mm anneal	19( )	51	46	71 R$_f$	0.314	8.69	1870	0.09	9.1	312	115	17.5
	Zn	25	½ hard	60( )	73	12	80 R$_b$ "								
	Ni	10	Hard	75( )	86	4	89 "								
High-silicon bronze, (A)	Cu	94.8 min	0.035 min anneal	25( )	60	60	62 "	0.308	8.53	1780–1880	0.09	10.0	252	150	15
	Si	3	½ hard	45( )	78	17	87 "								
			Hard	58( )	94	8	93 "								
			Hot rolled	25( )	64	60	72 "								
Aluminum bronze, 5% nickel	Cu	81.5	Extruded and sized	50(")	110	9	98 "	0.273	7.54	1890–1910		8.5	551		17
	Al	10													
	Ni	5													
	Fe	2.5													
	Mn	1													
Aluminum bronze, 9.5%	Cu	87.5	Extruded and sized	40(")	85	15	87 "	0.276	7.65	1890–1910		9.0	551		17
	Al	9.5													
	Fe	3													
Aluminum bronze, 8%	Cu	90.5	As rolled	32(")	72	35	80 "	0.279	7.73	1910–1940		9.0	609		18
	Al	7													
	Fe	2.5													
Nickel (pure)	Ni	99.9	Annealed	8.5	46	28	85	0.322	8.91	2650	0.11	7.4	575	37	30

Metal	Nominal Composition (%)	Condition and Temper	Yield Strength, 1000 psi	Tensile Strength, 1000 psi	Elongation in 2 in. (%)	Hardness	Density lb./in.³	Specific Gravity	Melting Range (°F)	Specific Heat (32-212°F) Btu/lb./°F	Coeff. Therm. Exp., (32-212°F) 10^{-6} in./in./°F	Thermal Conductivity, (room temp.) Btu/sq. ft./in./hr./°F	Electrical Resistivity, (68°F) ohms/cir. mil ft.	Tensile Modulus of Elasticity, 10^6 psi
Nickel (wrought)	Ni 99.0 min	Annealed	20	70	40	100	0.321	8.89	2615–2635	0.11	7.2	420	57	30
		Hot rolled	25	75	40	110								
		Cold drawn	70	95	25	170								
		Cold rolled[1]	95	105	5	210								
Low-carbon nickel	Ni 99.0 min, C 0.02 max	Annealed	15	60	50	90	0.321	8.89	2615–2635	0.11	7.2	420	50	30
Nickel (cast)	Ni Rem., Si 2.0, Fe 1.25	Sand cast[2]	25	50	25	100	0.301	8.34	2540–2600	0.11	7.2	410	125	21.5
"D" Nickel	Ni 95, Mn 4.5	Annealed	35	75	40	140	0.317	8.78	2500–2600	0.11	7.4	335	110	30
		Hot rolled	50	90	35	150								
		Cold drawn	80	100	25	190								
"E" Nickel	Ni 98, Mn 2	Annealed	35	75	40	140	0.320	8.86	2570–2600	0.11	7.4	335	85	30
		Hot rolled	50	90	35	150								
		Cold drawn	80	100	25	190								
"Dura-nickel"	Ni 94, Al 4.4	Hot rolled	50	105	35	180	0.298	8.26	2615–2635	0.104	7.1	128	280	30
		Hot rolled[3]	130	170	15	320					7.3	137	260	
		Cold drawn[3]	90	120	25	220								
		Cold drawn[3]	175	210	15	340								

Material	Composition	Condition											
Monel (wrought)[9]	Ni 67 Cu 30	Annealed Hot rolled Cold drawn[1] Cold rolled[1]	35 50 80 100	75 90 100 110	40 35 25 5	125 150 190 240	0.319	8.84	2370–2460	0.13	7.8	180	290	26
Monel (cast)	Ni 63 Cu 32 Si 1.25	Sand cast	35	80	35	135	0.312	8.63	2400–2450	0.13	6.8	180	320	19
"R" monel	Ni 67 Cu 30 S 0.035	Hot rolled Cold drawn	45 75	85 90	35 25	145 180	0.319	8.84	2370–2460	0.13	7.8	180	290	26
"K" monel	Ni 66 Cu 29 Al 2.75	Hot rolled Hot rolled[3] Cold drawn Cold drawn[3]	45 110 85 130	100 150 115 170	40 25 25 20	160 280 210 290	0.306	8.47	2400–2460	0.13	7.8	130	350	20
"H" monel	Ni 65 Cu 29.5 Si 3.0	Sand Cast[2]	60	100	15	210	0.305	8.48	2350–2400	0.13	6.8	180	370	20
"S" monel	Ni 63 Cu 30 Si 4	Sand cast[4] Sand cast[2] Sand cast[3]	70 100 100	90 130 130	3 2 2	275 320 350	0.302	8.36	2300–2350	0.13	6.8	180	380	21
Inconel (wrought)	Ni 77.5 Cr 15 Fe 7.5	Annealed Hot rolled Cold drawn Cold drawn[1]	35 60 90 110	85 100 115 135	45 35 20 5	150 180 200 260	0.307	8.51	2540–2600	0.11	6.4	104	590	31

[1] Hard temper
[2] As cast
[3] Age hardened
[4] Annealed
[9] 326 Monel same as Monel except Ni content 55–60%

173

APPENDIX A (Continued)

Metal	Nominal Composition (%)	Condition and Temper	Yield Strength, 1000 psi	Tensile Strength, 1000 psi	Elongation in 2 in. (%)	Hardness	Density lb./in.³	Specific Gravity	Melting Range (°F)	Specific Heat (32-212°F) Btu/lb./°F	Coeff. Therm. Exp., (32-212°F) 10^{-6} in./in./°F	Thermal Conductivity, (room temp.) Btu/sq. ft./in./hr./°F	Electrical Resistivity, (68°F) ohms/cir. mil ft.	Tensile Modulus of Elasticity, 10^6 psi
Inconel (cast)	Ni 78.0 Fe 6.0 Cr 13.5 Si 2.0	Sand cast[2]	40	85	20	175	0.300	8.30	2500-2550	0.11	6.4			23
Inconel "X"	Ni 73 Cr 15.0 Fe 7.0 Ti 2.5 Al 0.7 Cb 1.0	Annealed Hot rolled[3]	50 120	115 180	50 25	200 360	0.300	8.30	2540-2600	0.105	7.6	102	750	31
Inconel "W"	Ni 73.0 Cr 15.5 Fe 7.0 Al 0.7 Ti 2.5	Annealed Annealed[3]	45 100	105 150	55 27	180 260	0.301	8.31	2540-2600	0.105	7.6	102	750	31
80 Ni 20 Cr alloy (wrought)	Ni 78 Cr 19	Cold drawn[4] Cold drawn[1]	60	95 165	30 1	90 R_b 102 "	0.303	8.40	2550	0.107	7.3	104	650	31
60 Ni 15 Cr alloy (wrought)	Ni 61 Fe Bal. Cr 15.5	Hot rolled Cold drawn[4] Cold drawn[1]	60	110 95 160	35	200	0.303	8.4	2450-2550	0.107	7.6	94	675	31

Material	Composition	Condition											
60 Ni 15 Cr alloy (cast)	Ni 60 / Fe Bal. / Cr 14	Cast²	45	65	2	180	0.303	8.4	2450–2550	0.136	6.2	96	675	30.5
"Hastelloy" Alloy A	Ni Bal. / Mo 21 / Fe 19	Sand cast⁴	48	73	12	168	0.318	8.80	2370–2425	0.094	6.1	116	762	24
		Hot rolled⁴	44	110	50	175								27
		Investment cast²	45	76	21	173								—
"Hastelloy" Alloy B	Ni Bal. / Mo 28 / Fe 5	Sand cast⁴	58	80	8	207	0.334	9.24	2410–2460	0.091	5.6	78.5	812	26.5
		Hot rolled⁴	60	135	50	201								30.8
		Investment cast²	61	85	14	216								28.5
"Hastelloy" Alloy C	Ni Bal. / Mo 16 / Cr 16 / Fe 5 / W 4	Investment cast²	60	80	7	225	0.323	8.94	2320–2380	0.092	6.3	87	800	—
		Sand cast⁴	58	78	8	218								24.5
		Hot rolled	55	130	45	211								26
"Hastelloy" Alloy D	Ni Bal. / Si 10 / Cu 3	Sand cast⁴	118	118	0–2 (in 1")	390	0.282	7.80	2030–2050	0.108	6.1	145	680	28.9
"Ilium" G	Ni Bal. / Cr 22 / Fe 6 / Mo 6 / Cu 6 / Mn 1.25 / Si .65	Cast²	57	68	7	185	0.310	8.58	2375	0.105	7.5	84	735	26.8

¹ Hard temper
² As cast
³ Age hardened
⁴ Annealed

Appendix A (Continued)

Metal	Nominal Composition (%)	Condition and Temper	Yield Strength, 1000 psi	Tensile Strength, 1000 psi	Elongation in 2 in. (%)	Hardness	Density lb./in.³	Specific Gravity	Melting Range (°F)	Specific Heat (32–212°F) Btu/lb./°F	Coeff. Therm. Exp., (32–212°F) 10^{-6} in./in./°F	Thermal Conductivity, (room temp) Btu/sq. ft./in./hr./°F	Electrical Resistivity, (68°F) ohms/cir. mil ft.	Tensile Modulus of Elasticity, 10^6 psi
Tungsten	W	Sintered		18.5	—	225	0.697	19.3	6170 ±35	0.034	2.2	1160	32.9	50
		Drawn 15 min.		285	1–4	375								
Molybdenum	Mo	Drawn 14 min.	57–85	215–240	2–5	155–250	0.368	10.3	4760	0.065	3.0	1010	31.1	42
M1A ("Dow-metal" M)	Mg Bal. Mn 1.2	Hot rolled	—	33	12	—	0.064	1.76	1198–1200	0.25	14.4	870	30	6.5
		Cold rolled	28	37	7	56								
		Annealed	18	33	16	48								
Silver (pure)	Ag 99.9 plus	Annealed	12	23	45	30	0.379	10.50	1760	0.056	10.9	2900	9.55	11
		Cold rolled[1]	38	43	6	90								
Gold (pure)	Au 99.99	Annealed	0PL	17	45	25	0.698	19.32	1945	0.031	7.8	2000	14	12
		Cold rolled[1]	30 "	32	4	60								
Platinum (pure)	Pt 99.99	Annealed	10 "	24	24	40	0.772	21.40	3225	0.032	4.9	480	64	21
		Cold rolled[1]	27 "	36	2.5	100								
Platinum (commercial)	Pt 99 plus	Annealed	6.5 "	23	29	57	0.772	21.40	3225	0.032	4.9	480	72	22.6
		Cold rolled[1]	27 "	37	3.5	113								
Iridium-platinum 10%	Pt Bal. Ir 10	Annealed	30 "	53	27	110	0.778	21.53	3230–3270		4.93		150	
		Cold rolled[1]	54 "	82	2.5	170								

Material	Composition	Condition												
Rhodium platinum 10%	Pt Bal., Rh 10	Annealed	17PL	47	37	65	0.742	20.55	3345				114	
		Cold rolled[1]	56″	84	3	160								
Palladium (commercial)	Pd 99.5	Annealed	5″	30	40	44	0.432	11.98	2830	0.058	6.5	490	65	17
		Cold rolled[1]	32″	47	1.5	106								
Palladium (hard)	Pd Bal., Ru 4, Rh 1	Annealed	28″	59	23		0.432	11.98	2860					
		Cold rolled[1]	46″	72	3									
Tantalum	Ta 99.9+	Annealed or unannealed sheet		42 to 178	45–25 (in 1″)	55 to 125	0.60	16.6	5425	0.036	3.57	375	90.2	27
Wrought iron	Fe Bal., Slag 2.5	Hot rolled	30	48	30 (in 8″)	100	0.278	7.70	2750	0.11	6.7	418	70	29
Ingot iron	Fe 99.9+	Hot rolled	29	45	26	90	0.284	7.86	2795	0.108	6.5	494	57	30.1
		Annealed	19	38	45	67								
Gray cast iron	C 3.1, Si 1.8, Mn 0.7, Fe Bal.	Cast[2]	None	32	0.5 max.	180	0.260	7.20	2075		6.0	310	400	13 ± 1.5
Malleable iron	C 2.5, Si 1, Mn 0.55	Cast[2]	36.5YP	55	20	130	0.264	7.32	2250	0.122	6.6	435	180	25

[1] Hard temper   [2] As cast

Material	Nominal Composition (%)	Condition and Temper	Yield Strength, 1000 psi	Tensile Strength, 1000 psi	Elongation in 2 in. (%)	Hardness	Density lb/in.³	Specific Gravity	Melting Range (°F)	Specific Heat (32-212°F) Btu/lb./°F	Coeff. Therm. Exp., (32-212°F) 10^{-6} in./in./°F	Thermal Conductivity, (room temp.) Btu/sq. ft./in./hr./°F	Electrical Resistivity, (68°F) ohms/cir. mil ft.	Tensile Modulus of Elasticity, 10^6 psi
"Ni-Tensyl-iron"	C 2.7 Si 1.5 Mn 0.8 Ni 2.3 Cr 0.3 Fe Bal. Mo 0.4	Cast[2] Cast[10]	30PL 40PL	40 100		220 350	0.260	7.20	2150		6.5	320		20 ± 1.5
"Ni-Resist" Type 1	C 2.8 Si 1.5 Mn 1.0 Ni 14.0 Cr 2.0 Cu 7.0 Fe Bal.	Cast[2]		30	2	150	0.270	7.48	2150		10.6	275	1050	14.5
"Ni-Resist," Type 2	C 2.8 Si 1.8 Mn 1.3 Ni 20 Cr 2.5 Fe Bal.	Cast[2]		30	2	150	0.270	7.48	2150		10.3	275	1050	14.5 ± 1.5

Material	Composition	Condition										
Ductile iron (Mg containing)	C 3.4 Si 2.5 Mn 0.7 P 0.1 max. Ni 1.5 Mg 0.06 Fe Bal.	Cast² Cast⁴	70 55	100 70	3 20	245 160	} 0.26	7.2	2100	7.5	360	25
Ductile "Ni-Resist" (Mg containing)	C 2.8 Si 2.5 Mn 1 P 0.01 max. Ni 20 Cr 2 Mg 0.1 Fe Bal.	Cast⁴	35	60	10	175	0.268	7.4	2250	10.4	610	18.5
"Ni-Hard", low-carbon	C 2.7 Si 0.6 Mn 0.5 Ni 4.5 Cr 1.5 Fe Bal.	Sand cast² Chill cast²			55 75	550 625	} 0.275	7.70	2150	4.8		
"Ni-Hard" high-carbon	C 3.0 Si 0.6 Mn 0.5 Ni 4.0 Cr 1.5 Fe Bal.	Sand cast² Chill cast²			30 80	600 700	} 0.275	7.70	2150	4.8		

² As cast
⁴ Annealed
¹⁰ Heat treated

179

Metal	Nominal Composition (%)		Condition and Temper	Yield Strength, 1000 psi	Tensile Strength, 1000 psi	Elongation in 2 in. (%)	Hardness	Density lb./in.³	Specific Gravity	Melting Range (°F)	Specific Heat (32–212°F), Btu/lb./°F	Coeff. Therm. Exp., (32–212°F), 10⁻⁶, in./in./°F	Thermal Conductivity, (room temp.) Btu/sq. ft./in./hr./°F	Electrical Resistivity, (68°F) ohms/cir. mil ft.	Tensile Modulus of Elasticity, 10⁶ psi
Carbon steel SAE 1020	Fe	Bal.	Annealed	40	60	35	130	0.284	7.86	2760	0.116	6.5	357	101	30
	Mn	0.45	Hot rolled	45	69	31	146								
	Si	0.25	Hardened[11]	80	104	6	205								
	C	0.20	Hardened[12]	62	90	22	175								
Cast carbon steel	Fe	Bal.	Cast[4]	40	72	26	140	0.283	7.84	2745	0.107	6.7	400	90	30
	Mn	0.70	Cast[13]	45	80	30	160								
	Si	0.40	Cast[14]	60	90	25	185								
	C	0.30													
Cast alloy steel	Fe	Bal.	Cast[4]	60	105	20	225	0.284	7.87	2745	0.107	6.7			30
	Ni	1.75	Cast[15]	95	120	17	260								
	Mn	0.80	Cast[16]	135	150	13.5	325								
	Cr	0.75													
	C	0.30													
	Mo	0.25													
Stainless steel Type 301	Fe	Bal.	Annealed	35	100	65	160	0.29	8.02	2550–2590	0.12	8.0	113	435	29
	Cr	17	C. R. 52%	164	190	32	385								
	Ni	7													
	C	0.11													
Stainless steel Type 302	Fe	Bal.	Annealed	30	90	55	160	0.29	8.02	2550–2590	0.12	8.0	113	435	28
	Cr	18	C. R. 51%	156	177	5.5									
	Ni	9													
	C	0.10													

Material		Condition											
Stainless steel Type 304	Fe Bal. Cr 19 Ni 9.0 C 0.08	Annealed C. R. 50%	30 152	85 167	50 8	160	0.29	8.02	2550–2650	0.12	8.0	113	435	28
Cast stainless steel Type 304	Fe Bal. Cr 19 Ni 9 C 0.1	Cast[4]	35	79	54	131	0.286	7.92	2550–2590	0.12	8.0	110	420	29
Stainless steel Type 309	Fe Bal. Cr 23 Ni 13 C 0.20	Annealed C. R. 45%	30 132	82 144	50 6	165	0.29	8.02	2550–2650	0.12	8.0	108	470	29
Stainless steel Type 310	Fe Bal. Cr 25 Ni 20 C 0.25	Annealed C. R. 50%	40 135	100 145	50 3	165	0.29	8.02	2550–2650	0.12	8.0	96	470	30
Stainless steel Type 316	Fe Bal. Cr 17 Ni 12 Mo 2.5 C 0.10	Annealed C. R. 49%	40 136	90 148	50 6	165 275	0.292	7.94	2500–2550	0.12	8.8	114	445	29
Cast stainless steel Type 316	Fe Bal. Cr 19 Ni 9 Mo 2.1 C .05	Cast[4]	35	83	60	161	0.286	7.92	2550–2590	0.12	8.0	110	479	29

[4] Annealed
[11] Water quenched, drawn at 200°F
[12] Water quenched, drawn at 1000°F
[13] Normalized at 1200°F
[14] Water quenched, drawn at 1250°F
[15] Normalized at 1150°F
[16] Water quenched, drawn at 1150°F

181

Metal	Nominal Composition (%)	Condition and Temper	Yield Strength, 1000 psi	Tensile Strength, 1000 psi	Elongation in 2 in. (%)	Hardness	Density lb./in.³	Specific Gravity	Melting Range (°F)	Specific Heat (32-212°F) Btu/lb./°F	Coeff. Therm. Exp., (32-212°F) 10^{-6} in./in./°F	Thermal Conductivity, (room temp.) Btu/sq. ft./in./hr./°F	Electrical Resistivity, (68°F) ohms/cir. mil ft.	Tensile Modulus of Elasticity, 10^6 psi
Stainless steel Type 321	Fe Bal. Cr 18 Ni 10 C 0.08 Ti 5 X C	Annealed C. R. 50%	35 141	85 160	50 4.0	160 300	0.292	7.94	2550-2600	0.12	8.3	113	435	28
Stainless steel Type 347	Fe Bal. Cr 18 Ni 11 C 0.08 Cb 10 X C	Annealed C. R. 52%	40 144	90 169	50 4.0	160	0.292	7.94	2550-2600	0.12	8.3	113	435	28
Stainless steel "Armco" 17-7 PH	Fe Bal. Cr 17 Ni 7 Al 1 C 0.09	Annealed Cold rolled Cold drawn	40 220 290	130 235 300	30 3 5	170 440 515	0.276	7.65			6.1		505	29.5
Stainless steel Type 410	Fe Bal. Cr 12.5 C 0.15	Annealed Heat treated	40 115	75 150	30 15	150 300	0.28	7.75	2700-2790	0.11	5.1	173	340	29
Stainless steel Type 414	Fe Bal. Cr 12.5 Ni 1.75 C 0.15	Annealed Heat treated	80 150	100 200	22 17	217 387	0.28	7.75	2600-2700	0.11	5.5	173	420	29

Material	Composition	Condition						Sp. gr.	Melting point					
Stainless steel Type 420	Fe Bal., Cr 13, C 0.30	Annealed	60	98	28	180	0.28	7.75	2650–2750	0.11	5.5	173	330	29
		Heat treated	200	250	8	480								
Stainless steel Type 430	Fe Bal., Cr 16, C 0.12	Annealed	45	70	30	150	0.28	7.75	2600–2750	0.11	5.1	165	360	29
		C. R. 45%	111	115	2.5	217								
Stainless steel Type 431	Fe Bal., Cr 16, Ni 1.75, C 0.20	Annealed	85	120	25	250	0.280	7.75	2600–2700	0.11	6.5	140	430	29
		Heat treated	150	195	20	400								
Stainless steel Type 446	Fe Bal., Cr 25, C 0.35	Annealed	50	80	30	165	0.27	7.45	2550–2700	0.12	5.7	145	405	29
Invar	Fe Bal., Ni 36	Annealed	42	70	41	130	0.289	8.09	2600	0.123	0.6	73	480	21
		Hot rolled	50	75	37	140								
Stainless steel Type 312	Fe Bal., Cr 29, Ni 9	Hot rolled	45	90	30	170								
Cast 28 Cr 10 Ni alloy ACI type HE	Fe Bal., Cr 29, Ni 9	Cast[2]	45(.5%)	85	10	200	0.277	7.67		0.14	10.5			22
Stainless steel Type 330	Fe Bal., Ni 36, Cr 16	Hot rolled	55	100	35	200	0.284	7.86	2515	0.11	6.3	90	600	
		Cold drawn[1]		80										
		Cold drawn[4]		150										

[1] Hard temper
[2] As cast
[4] Annealed

183

Metal	Nominal Composition (%)		Condition and Temper	Yield Strength, 1000 psi	Tensile Strength, 1000 psi	Elongation in 2 in. (%)	Hardness	Density lb./in.^{3}	Specific Gravity	Melting Range (°F)	Specific Heat (32-212°F) Btu/lb./°F	Coeff. Therm. Exp., (32-212°F) 10^{-6} in./in./°F	Thermal Conductivity, (room temp) Btu/sq. ft./in./hr./°F	Electrical Resistivity, (68°F) ohms/cir. mil ft.	Tensile Modulus of Elasticity, 10^6 psi
Cast 35 Ni 15 Cr ACI type HT	Fe Ni Cr	Bal. 36 16	Cast[2]	38(.5%)	69	10	192	0.290	8.04		0.135	9.7			23
Iron-silicon alloy	Fe Si C Mn	Bal. 14.5 0.8 0.35	Cast[2]	17	17	0	500	0.253	7.00	2300	0.12	3.6	360	380	
"Durichlor"	Fe Si Mo C	Bal. 14.5 3 0.8	Cast[2]	17	17	0	500	0.254	7.04	2350	0.12	3.6	360	380	
"Durimet T"	Fe Ni Cr Mo Si Cu	Bal. 22 19 2.5 1 1	Cast[4] Hot rolled[4]	35 45	70 85	40 50	140 140	}0.283	7.85	2650	0.12	7.8	145	580	22.7 27.8

[2] As cast   [4] Annealed

184

AWS STANDARDS AND BOOKS

A. Fundamentals of Welding

A2.0–47	Standard Welding Symbols	$ 1.00
A2.1-47	Symbols Wall Chart	.50
A3.0-49	Standard Welding Terms and Their Definitions	1.00
A3.1-49	Master Chart of Welding Processes and Process Charts	.50
A3.0 and A3.1 together		1.25
A4.0-42	Standard Methods for Mechanical Testing of Welds (with 1945 Supplement)	.50
*A5.1-55T	Specifications for Mild Steel Arc-Welding Electrodes (Tentative)	.40
*A5.2-46T	Specifications for Iron and Steel Gas-Welding Rods (Tentative)	.40
*A5.4-55T	Specifications for Corrosion-Resisting Chromium and Chromium-Nickel Steel Welding Electrodes (Tentative)	.40
*A5.5-54T	Specifications for High Tensile and Low-Alloy Steel Arc-Welding Electrodes-Covered (Tentative)	.40
*A5.6-53T	Specifications for Copper and Copper-Alloy Welding Electrodes (Tentative)	.40
*A5.7-52T	Specifications for Copper and Copper-Alloy Welding Rods (Tentative)	.40
*A5.8-52T	Specifications for Brazing Filler Metal (Tentative)	.40
*A5.9-53T	Specifications for Corrosion-Resisting Chromium and Chromium-Nickel Steel Welding Rods and Bare Electrodes (Tentative)	.40
*A5.10-54T	Specifications for Aluminum and Aluminum-Alloy Welding Rods and Bare Electrodes (Tentative)	.40
*A5.11-54T	Specifications for Nickel and Nickel-Base Alloy Covered Welding Electrodes (Tentative)	.40
*A5.12-55T	Specifications for Tungsten Arc Welding Electrodes (Tentative)	.40
A6.0-52	Safe Practices for Welding and Cutting Containers That Have Held Combustibles	.50
A6.1-55	Recommended Safe Practices for Inert-Gas Metal-Arc Welding	.50
Z49.1-50	Safety in Electric and Gas Welding and Cutting Operations, American Standard	.50

B. Training, Inspection and Control

B1.1-45	Inspection Handbook for Manual Metal-Arc Welding	$ 2.00
B2.1-45	Code of Minimum Requirements for Instruction of Welding Operators: Part A—Arc Welding of Steel	.75
B2.2-44T	Code of Minimum Requirements for Instruction of Welding Operators: Part B-1—Oxy-Acetylene Welding of Steel-Aircraft	.75
B3.0-41T	Standard Qualification Procedure	.50

C. Processes

C1.1-50	Recommended Practices for Resistance Welding	$ 1.00
C1.2-53T	Recommended Practices for Spot Welding Aluminum and Aluminum Alloys	1.00
C2.1-50T	Recommended Practices for Metallizing: Part IA—Metallizing Shafts or Similar Objects Part II—Metallizing—Safety Recommendations	.75
C2.2-52T	Recommended Practices for Metallizing: Part IB—Application of Aluminum and Zinc for Protection of Iron and Steel	.50

185

C2.3-54T   Recommended Practices for Metallizing:
Part IC—Application of Metallized Coatings to Protect Against Heat Corrosion............................... .50

D. Industrial Applications

D1.0-46	Standard Code for Arc and Gas Welding in Building Construction....	$ 1.00
D2.0-47	Standard Specifications for Welded Highway and Railway Bridges...	1.00
D3.3-53	Rules for Welding Piping in Marine Construction—Carbon Steels......	.25
D3.4-52T	Rules for Welding Piping in Marine Construction—Ferritic Alloy Steels......	.50
D4.0-44T	Weldability Standards for Alternate Aircraft Steels.........	.25
D5.1-52	Rules for Field Welding of Steel Storage Tanks............	.50
*D5.2-52	AWWA-AWS Standard Specifications for Elevated Steel Water Tanks, Standpipes and Reservoirs......	.70
*D7.0-49	AWWA-AWS Standard Specifications for Field Welding of Steel Water Pipe Joints......	.25
D8.1-46T	Recommended Practices for Automotive Flash Butt Welding.	.50
D8.2-48T	Survey of Automatic Arc and Gas Welding Processes as Used in the Automotive Industry......	.30
D8.3-50T	Recommended Practices for Salvaging Automotive Gray Iron Castings by Welding......	.50
D10.1-53T	Recommended Practices for Postweld Heat Treatment of Austenitic Weldments......	.50
D10.2-54T	Recommended Practices for Repair Welding of Cast Iron Pipe, Valves and Fittings......	.50

Books

* "Welding Handbook," Third Edition, 1651 pages, cloth bound.

Members......	$ 9.00
Nonmembers—U. S. A. and Canada......	12.00
Nonmembers—Elsewhere......	13.00

* "Welding Metallurgy," Second Edition, revised by G. E. Linnert, 505 pages, cloth bound. 1949...... 3.00

"Practical Design of Welded Steel Structures," H. M. Priest, 153 pages, cloth bound, 1943...... 1.00

Binder

*Binder for all Codes and Standards in Groups A, B, C and D.

Members......	3.00
Nonmembers......	3.50

* NOTE: 25% discount to A and B members and 15% discount to C members of AWS on orders for individual copies of any codes, standards and books listed above except starred items.

Special discount on all quantity orders of 25 or more copies of any code, standard or book.

Above prices and other information subject to change without notice. Consult Order Form for latest information.

INDEX